TUTTLE
12/90 $150.00

THE UNITED STATES NAVY
1776 to 1815

The PHŒNIX and the ROSE Engaged by the ENEMY'S FIRE SHIPS and GALLEYS on the 16 Aug.t 1776

Engraved from the Original Picture by D. Serres from a sketch of Sir James Wallace.

PHOENIX AND ROSE ENGAGED BY AMERICAN FIRE SHIPS IN THE HUDSON RIVER,

AUGUST 16, 1776

Engraved from a picture by Dominic Serres after a sketch by Sir James Wallace

(See No. 1)

THE
UNITED STATES NAVY
1776 TO 1815

DEPICTED IN AN EXHIBITION

OF PRINTS OF AMERICAN NAVAL ENGAGEMENTS

AND AMERICAN NAVAL COMMANDERS

HELD AT THE GROLIER CLUB

NOVEMBER 19, 1942 TO JANUARY 17, 1943

NEW YORK

THE GROLIER CLUB

1942

TABLE OF CONTENTS

LIST OF ILLUSTRATIONS

[viii]

INTRODUCTION

An exhibition of prints of American naval engagements and American naval commanders seems timely. Never before has this country been so dependent upon its Navy as in these critical days of all-out war through the greater part of the world. The story of our Navy in its early days is told to a large extent by the prints, mostly contemporaneous, depicting the victories, defeats and other significant events of that period.

The birth of the United States Navy occurred during the Revolutionary War. Our naval force emerged from swaddling clothes a few years later to meet the necessities occasioned by interference with American commerce on the high seas by Algiers and later by France. It was then that the Navy Department was established and the famous 44-gun American frigates constructed. The most famous ship of this class was the *Constitution*, popularly known in succeeding days as *Old Ironsides*.

The War with Tripoli, commencing in 1801, provided a training ground for those who were destined to command our men-of-war in the War of 1812. In this conflict with Great Britain, the United States Navy reached maturity. Despite the small number of naval vessels then under the American flag, outstanding victorious single-ship and fleet engagements with the world's greatest naval power established a reputation, prestige and esprit-de-corps which has ever remained a cherished and respected heritage of the United States Navy.

This exhibition is limited to prints dealing with our Navy and its more prominent officers from the time of the Revolution through the War with Algiers in 1815. Our aim has been to include in the showing all approximately contemporaneous prints of American naval engagements of this period, available to the Committee, quite irrespective of the outcome of the battle, or of the American or foreign origin of the print. Except in a few cases, various states of the same plate are not exhibited. Limited space has compelled a selective showing of engraved portraits of American naval officers of this era.

In the following description of the prints, the portion printed in italics is a complete copy of the major text of the inscription on the face of the print. No attempt has been made to reproduce the size or character of type appearing on the print. The order of arrangement of such text on the print has not been followed exactly in all instances. It has seemed more logical and orderly to adopt a uniform scheme of arrangement—first giving the title of the view; then the names of artist and engraver, if stated; and ending with the publication data, if any. Measurements are of the engraved or lithographed surfaces, and are not more exact than a sixteenth of an inch. The vertical dimension is first given, followed by the horizontal measurement.

References in the succeeding text are to the below mentioned standard works on engravings and lithographs: Stauffer—*American Engravers Upon Copper and Steel*, by David McNeely Stauffer; Fielding—*American Engravers Upon Copper and Steel*, by Mantle Fielding; Parker—*Naval Battles From the Collection of Prints Formed and Owned by Sir Charles Leopold Cust*, by Harry Parker; Stokes and Haskell—*American Historical Prints*, by I. N. Phelps Stokes and Daniel C. Haskell; H. T. Peters's Currier & Ives, and America On Stone—*Currier & Ives, Printmakers to the American People*, and *America On Stone*, both by Harry T. Peters.

Biographical sketches of artists and engravers are based largely upon the data contained in the above mentioned books, the greater part being derived from the works of Stauffer and Fielding. *The Dictionary of American Biography* has been the principal source for the biographical sketches of the naval commanders.

The historical accounts of the naval actions and other episodes covered by the prints included in this exhibition are based primarily upon Capt. Dudley W. Knox's excellent work *A History of the United States Navy*, published in 1936 by G. P. Putnam's Sons; *The Naval War of 1812*, by Theodore Roosevelt (New York, 1882); *The Naval Monument*, by Abel Bowen (Boston, 1816); *American Naval Battles*, published by Charles Gaylord (Boston, 1837); *A History of the United States Navy*, by Edgar Stanton Maclay (New Edition, New York, 1898); and *A History of American Privateers*, by Edgar Stanton Maclay (New York, 1899).

This exhibition has been made possible through the co-operation and assistance willingly afforded to the Committee by many interested individuals, both within and outside The Grolier Club. The President of the United States graciously offered to lend such prints as might be desired from his collection at The White House and from The Franklin D. Roosevelt Library at Hyde Park, N. Y. Mrs. Francis P. Garvan kindly made available the extensive collection of naval prints owned by the Estate of Francis P. Garvan, now lent to Yale University. Many choice and rare prints, needed for the completeness of the showing, were obtained through the courtesy of Henry O. Havemeyer, Hall Park McCullough, Henry Graves, Jr.,Dr. Eugene H. Pool, Valentine Hollingsworth, William H. Coverdale, and the Peabody Museum at Salem, Mass. A considerable number of prints has been provided by members of the Committee, including items from the large and well-known collection of Beverley R. Robinson.

Valuable counsel has been given to the Committee by such experienced men in this field as Robert Fridenberg, Herman Wunderlich, O. M. Torrington, Harry MacNeill Bland, Russell W. Thorpe, Charles E. Goodspeed and Charles D. Childs, to whom the Committee is also grateful for the loan of a number of prints. We acknowledge gratefully the guidance and advice received from Captain Harry A. Baldridge, Curator of the Naval Academy Museum at Annapolis, Md.; Captain Dudley W. Knox, Officer in Charge of Office of Naval Records and Library, Navy Department, Washington, D. C.; Theodore Sizer, Director of the Yale University Art Gallery; and John Marshall Phillips, Curator of the Mabel Brady Garvan Collections at Yale University. Helpful support came from the officials of The Grolier Club, and, in particular, from George L. McKay, Curator, and Miss Ruth S. Granniss, Librarian. To all of the individuals above mentioned and to the others who assisted in a lesser degree, the Committee expresses its deep appreciation.

In a publication of this kind, prepared in a brief space of time, errors and omissions are probably inevitable. Any information in the way of corrections or additions to the list of naval prints will be welcomed by the Committee, and should be sent to The Grolier Club, 47 East 60th Street, New York, N. Y.

IRVING S. OLDS, *Chairman*
HARRY S. NEWMAN
ALFRED W. PAINE
BEVERLEY R. ROBINSON
ALEXANDER O. VIETOR
Grolier Club Committee

New York, N. Y.
November 19, 1942

PART I

REVOLUTIONARY WAR

THE PHOENIX AND THE ROSE
AUGUST 16, 1776

At the time this incident of the Revolutionary War occurred, New York and Manhattan Island had not been occupied by the British Army. Lord Howe took possession a few weeks thereafter.

In July 1776, a squadron of British naval vessels had sailed up the Hudson and anchored above New York. This offered a tempting opportunity for daring Colonials to try to destroy one or more of these ships. After five American galleys under the command of Lieutenant-Colonel Benjamin Tupper had failed in their first assault on August 3rd, a second attempt was made on the night of August 16, 1776.

A fire-ship, captained by Silas Talbot, succeeded in coming alongside of the British ship *Asia* of 64 guns and ignited her cargo of combustibles. The plan of action called for the crew of the fire-ship to jump into the river after setting fire to their tinder box, with the expectation of being picked up by comrades in waiting small boats.

Captain Talbot was severely burned in this courageous exploit, which, while brilliantly conceived and bravely carried out, did not accomplish the desired objective, although the British warships were forced to drop downstream.

The British fleet, present in the Hudson River, consisted of the ships *Phoenix, Rose, Asia,* and probably also the *Experiment,* which was then commanded by Sir James Wallace.

This was the first conflict of the Revolutionary War in the nature of a naval action.

I

The Phoenix and the Rose Engaged by the Enemy's Fire Ships and Galleys on the 16 Augst. 1776. ☆ Engrav'd from the Original Picture by D. Serres from a Sketch of Sir James Wallace's. ☆ Publish'd according to Act of Parliament April 2, 1778 by J. F. W. Des Barres, Esqr.

Aquatint. 10⅞ in. by 19⅝ in. Colored by hand. ☆ Second state, with the Palisades in the background. ☆ From The Atlantic Neptune. ☆ Stokes and Haskell B–100.

Frontispiece

I a

A first state of the above described print, without the Palisades in the background, is also included in this exhibition.

DOMINIC SERRES (1722–1793), after whose painting this print was made, is one of the best known of English marine painters. He came to England originally as a French prisoner of war, having been a sailor on a captured French ship. Serres studied art and was eventually elected a member of the Royal Academy. Serres was named by George III as Marine Painter to the King, a position subsequently held also by his son, John T. Serres (1759–1825).

BATTLE ON LAKE CHAMPLAIN
OCTOBER 11–13, 1776

This was an out-of-the-ordinary naval engagement, the command of the American ships being in the hands of an army officer, Benedict Arnold. It ended in the complete rout or destruction of the fleet of small vessels which the Americans had constructed on Lake Champlain in an effort to control that important artery of travel between Canada and the Hudson River district.

In the late summer of 1776 Lord Howe was attempting to wipe out the army under General Washington, which had been obliged to evacuate Brooklyn and New York and had retreated to the upper end of Manhattan Island and to White Plains. The British plan was to attack the American forces in the rear with a considerable army from Canada, which had to be transported over the length of Lake Champlain, due to the absence of paralleling roadways.

Benedict Arnold and his forces, retreating from the fruitless Quebec campaign, hastily constructed additional vessels on Lake Champlain to reinforce the then-existing tiny naval unit on that waterway so as to oppose the fleet which was being built by the British at the northern end of the Lake as a part of their program.

[2]

The engagement began on October 11, 1776, the British having twenty-five craft under the command of Captain Thomas Pringle and the Continentals fifteen under General Arnold. General Sir Guy Carleton was on board the British vessel *Maria*. At the end of two days of fighting, the entire American fleet had been captured, destroyed or otherwise dispersed.

Captain Dudley W. Knox in his recent authoritative work, *A History of the United States Navy*, G. P. Putnam's Sons, New York, 1936, comments on this engagement as follows: "No other naval force except the fleet of de Grasse did a greater service to the American cause during the war. It held up the projected British invasion from Canada until the season was too far advanced for that purpose. On that account Howe in the South abandoned his campaign against Washington east of the Hudson. . . ."

A port-hole frame with a bullet-shattered window glass from one of Arnold's vessels (presumably the schooner *Royal Savage* or the galley *Congress*), recovered from the bottom of Lake Champlain, is included in this exhibition.

2

[Engagement on Lake Champlain, October 11–13, 1776.]

References. N°. 1. Inflexible Ship. 2. Carleton Schooner 3. Maria Schooner. 4. Congress Galley, run a Shore, with other Vessels' blowing up. 5. Washington Galley strikeing. 6. Gun Boat coming up. ☆ *London, Printed for Robt. Sayer & Jn°. Bennett, N°. 53, Fleet Strand, as the Act directs. 23^d. Decr. 1776.* ☆ Artist and engraver not named.

Line engraving. 9⅝ in. by 13¾ in. In black and white.

Below the engraved view of the action is "A Description of the Engagement on Lake Champlain," consisting of copies of "a Letter from General Sir Guy Carleton to Lord George Germain, Principal Secretary of State for the American Department," dated "off Crown Point October 14, 1776"; "a Letter from Captain Douglas, of the *Isis*, to Mr. Stephens, Secretary to the Admiralty," dated "Quebec, 21st October 1776"; and "a Letter from Captain Thomas Pringle," dated "off Crown Point, the 15th of October, 1776." Printed at the right bottom corner of such description is "A circumstantial and authentic Account of the Roads and Distances from New York to Crown Point."

REFERENCES.

N.º *Inflexible Ship*. 2. *Carleton Schooner*. 3. *Maria Schooner*. 4. *Congress Gally, run a Shore, with other Veſsels*. 5. *Washington Gally, striking*. 6. *Gun Boat coming up*.

ACTION ON LAKE CHAMPLAIN BETWEEN A BRITISH FLEET AND AN AMERICAN FLEET
COMMANDED BY BENEDICT ARNOLD, OCTOBER 11–13, 1776

Printed for Robt. Sayer & Jno. Bennett, London

(See No. 2)

Printed for R. Sayer and J. Bennett, Map, Chart, and Print Sellers, No. 53, Fleet-Street. Price One shilling. ☆ Size of engraving and description, 20½ in. by 19½ in.
Illustrated

2 a

[Map of portion of Lake Champlain where the action shown in the preceding print took place, with the positions of the British and American fleets off Isle de Valcour indicated.]

The Attack and Defeat of the American Fleet under Benedict Arnold, By the Kings Fleet Commanded by Captn. Thos. Pringle, upon Lake Champlain, the 11th of October 1776. ☆ *Engraved by W^m. Faden Charing Cross:* ☆ *From a Sketch taken by an Officer on the Spot.* ☆ *London, Publish'd according to Act of Parliament, Decr. 3^d. 1776; by W^m. Faden (Successor to the late M^r. Jefferys Geographer to the King) Charing Cross.*

Engraved map. 10¹⁄₁₆ in. by 16 in. In black and white.

Below the map is: "An Account of the Expedition of the British Fleet on Lake Champlain, under the Command of Captain Thomas Pringle, and of the Defeat of the Rebel Fleet, commanded by Benedict Arnold, on the 11th and 13th of October, 1776. Taken from the Letters of Sir Guy Carleton, Captains Douglass and Pringle, dated off Crown Point, 15th October 1776. . . . Engraved by W. Faden (Successor to the late Mr. Jefferys, Geographer to the King) the Corner of St. Martin's-Lane, Charing-Cross, and to be had of Messrs. Wallis and Stonehouse, Booksellers, Ludgate-Street." ☆ Size of map and description, 19¹⁄₁₆ in. by 23⅜ in.

THE ACTION OFF MUD FORT IN THE
DELAWARE RIVER
OCTOBER 22, 1777

Lord Howe's occupation of Philadelphia in September 1777 was seriously hampered by his lack of control of the Delaware River below the city. The Continental forces had built defenses in this vicinity, two of their principal fortifications being Fort Mercer at Red Bank on the New Jersey shore and Fort Mifflin on an island in the Delaware nearly opposite.

[5]

Early in October 1777, the British dispatched a powerful fleet to the Delaware in order to break through the obstructions in the river erected by the Americans, overwhelm the Continental and Pennsylvania naval forces in the Delaware, silence these forts, and establish direct water communication between New York and the British Army in Philadelphia.

The combined American naval forces were commanded by Commodore John Hazelwood of the Pennsylvania Navy. They consisted of some of the men-of-war of the recently constituted Continental Navy, as well as a number of Pennsylvania naval craft, including floating batteries, rowing galleys, fire rafts and small boats. They were opposed by an infinitely stronger British force, embracing five ships of 44 guns or more each, together with smaller vessels. Silas Talbot, who commanded an American fire-ship in the *Phoenix* and *Rose* incident, also participated in this action.

On October 22, 1777, the British penetrated the lower obstructions in the river and attacked Fort Mercer by water and by land. Their ships were met by a part of the fleet under Commodore Hazelwood. The British naval force was driven down the Delaware. The British ships *Augusta*, 64 guns, and *Merlin*, 18 guns, ran aground, and were at once attacked. The *Augusta* caught fire, either through accident or by a shot from the American land batteries, and blew up. The *Merlin* was set on fire by her crew and abandoned. The assault on Fort Mercer by land was repulsed by Colonel Christopher Greene, with heavy British losses.

Several weeks later, the British renewed their attacks with great vigor, and on November 15, 1777, the Americans were obliged to evacuate Fort Mifflin. Fort Mercer was abandoned shortly thereafter. The larger American vessels then had to be destroyed to prevent their being taken by the enemy. Most of the small craft of the Pennsylvania Navy succeeded in retreating up the Delaware.

3

*Representation of the Action Off Mud Fort in the River Delaware; the Enemys fleet consisting of Frigates. Fire Ships. Galleys &c. attacking His Majestys Ships Augusta. Roebuck. Pearl. Liverpool and Merlin Sloop on the 22 of Oct*ʳ*. 1777. In which the Augusta took fire by Accident and the Merlin was burnt to prevent her falling into the hands of the Enemy. Position of the various ships engaged* indicated below the view. ☆ *Drawn on the Spot & Engraved by Lieu^t. W. Elliott.* ☆ *London Publis'd by W. Elliott 71 Park Street 17th of Feby. 1787.*

Aquatint. 17⅞ in. by 20¾ in. Colored by hand. ☆ Stokes and Haskell B–101. Mr. I. N. Phelps Stokes states: "Perhaps the most important of the very few naval prints of the Revolution, and the only important large one engraved in America."

The inscription on a similar print in the Stokes Collection at the New York Public Library differs from the above in a few respects. The word *Sloop* is omitted after *Merlin.* The date of the action is incorrectly given as *15th Novr. 1777.* The publication line reads: *Published as the Act directs by W. Elliott in Park Street 17th of Feby. 1787.*

Mr. Stokes's belief that this print was published in Philadelphia seems to be disproved by the inscription on the copy in the Graves Collection. Furthermore, no evidence has been found that William Elliott, the painter, was in America as late as 1787. The aquatint appears to be of a quality superior to that of contemporaneous similar engraving in America.

A small and a large painting of the engagement between the *Bon Homme Richard* and the *Serapis* by William Elliott, Royal Navy, are in the Naval Academy Museum at Annapolis, Md. It is presumed that this is the same W. Elliott who drew, engraved and published the above described print. William Elliott, the painter, was a Lieutenant and later a Captain in the Royal Navy. He was also a marine painter and between 1780 and 1790 gained some repute as a painter of naval actions. A painting of the engagement between the *Bon Homme Richard* and the *Serapis* was exhibited by Lieut. William Elliott, Royal Navy, at the Royal Academy in 1789. Elliott died at Leeds, England, in 1792.

3 a

[Map of that part of the Delaware River where the action shown in the preceding print took place.]

The Course of Delaware River from Philadelphia to Chester, Exhibiting the several works erected by the Rebels to defend its Passage, with the Attacks made upon them by His Majesty's Land & Sea Forces. ☆ *Engraved by William Faden Charing Cross April 30th. 1778.* ☆ The map shows the Colonial and British forts, batteries, etc.; also the positions of the various men-of-war and land forces. It contains an inset sketch of Fort Island, with Fort Mifflin.

Engraved map. 17¼ in. by 26¾ in. In black and white, slightly hand tinted.

SIR GEORGE COLLIER'S VICTORY
IN PENOBSCOT BAY
AUGUST 14, 1779

A strong British squadron of seven ships under the command of Sir George Collier sailed into Penobscot Bay on August 13, 1779. Its objective was to destroy or disperse the American naval force, partly Continental and partly Massachusetts, which had been assembled to assist in an attempt to recapture Castine, Maine. This town had been taken in June 1779, by a British force from Halifax. The next month American troops, under the protection of this naval unit, had been landed on the shores of Penobscot Bay in a counter offensive. This was known as the Penobscot Expedition, and was organized by the State of Massachusetts.

The British squadron found the American naval force in the Penobscot River on August 14, 1779. The marked superiority of the British force, headed by the 64-gun ship *Raisonnable*, compelled the American ships to flee. Two of these vessels were captured and the rest destroyed by their own crews.

4

Sir George Collier's victory in Penobscot Bay 1779. Baily Sculp. ☆ *Published Nov^n. 1, 1814, by Joyce Gold, Naval Chronicle Office, 103, Shee Lane, London.* ☆ Engraved by J. Baily after T. Whitcombe for The Naval Chronicle, Vol. XXXII. Aquatint. Oval. 5 in. by 9¼ in. In sepia. ☆ Parker 77–a.

LENT BY IRVING S. OLDS.

JOHN BAILEY (1750–1819) was the engraver of many of the naval prints contained as illustrations in J. Jenkins's *Naval Achievements of Great Britain*, Ralfe's *Naval Chronology*, and Gold's *The Naval Chronicle*.

THOMAS WHITCOMBE (1760–1825) was a prolific English marine painter, nearly one hundred prints of naval battles after his paintings being contained in the collection formed by Sir Charles Cust.

BON HOMME RICHARD AND SERAPIS

SEPTEMBER 23, 1779

This engagement is one of the most famous in all American naval history, not because of any decisive result therefrom, but rather by reason of the desperate nature of this first battle at sea of the infant American Navy and the personal courage and determination exhibited therein by John Paul Jones.

In February 1778, the Thirteen Continental States concluded an alliance with France. This gave to the American Navy the use of French bases. In August of the following year a squadron under the command of John Paul Jones set sail from L'Orient. After a raiding cruise around the west of Ireland and the north of Scotland, during which many prizes were taken, this American squadron encountered on September 23, 1779, off Flamborough Head on the east coast of England, the British ship *Serapis,* 50 guns, and the *Countess of Scarborough,* 20 guns, engaged in escorting a convoy returning from the Baltic. The flagship of Commodore Jones was the *Bon Homme Richard,* formerly an East Indian merchant ship, mounting 42 guns.

Commodore Jones, although unsupported at the outset by the three other vessels of his squadron, began the action by firing on the *Serapis.* A furious engagement at close quarters ensued between these two ships. Several hours of fighting alongside at point blank range left the *Bon Homme Richard* in a badly damaged condition. Most of her main battery of guns had been dismounted and silenced. When Captain Pearson of the *Serapis* at this point asked official confirmation of an American sailor's call for quarter, Jones replied: "I have not yet begun to fight."

His brave words became fact, when apparent defeat was converted into victory, largely due to the indomitable courage and superb fighting qualities of the American commander and the skill of his men aloft. The latter drove the British from their fighting tops and silenced the upper deck guns of the *Serapis* by dropping bombs and combustibles on her deck, a procedure which had a damaging effect upon the morale of the British crew. At this juncture, the American frigate *Alliance,* 32 guns, came to the aid of the *Bon Homme Richard,* causing confusion, however, at the outset by firing upon both the *Serapis* and the American flagship. At 10:30 P.M., the engagement having commenced at dusk, the *Serapis* struck her colors.

The damaged state of the *Bon Homme Richard* compelled Commodore Jones to transfer his flag to the captured *Serapis*. While every effort was made to save the *Bon Homme Richard*, she sank to the bottom of the North Sea some hours after the engagement.

During the main engagement between the *Bon Homme Richard* and the *Serapis*, the *Pallas*, 32 guns, one of Jones's squadron, engaged the British ship *Countess of Scarborough*, which was taken after an action of one hour.

The American squadron safely reached The Texel in the Netherlands on October 3, 1779, completing a never-to-be-forgotten cruise of several months.

English historians have discounted John Paul Jones's memorable victory on the ground that the important merchant fleet from the Baltic, which was under convoy, escaped capture.

5

*The memorable Engagement of Capt*ⁿ*. Pearson of the Serapis, with Paul Jones of the Bon Homme Richard & his Squadron, Sep. 23, 1779.* Similar inscription in French. ☆ *To Sir Richard Pearson Kn*^t*. whose Bravery & Conduct saved the Baltic Fleet under his Convoy tho' obliged to submit to a much superior force, This representation of that Action, Is with great Respect Inscribed, by his most obedient Servant, Richard Paton.* ☆ At the sides of the inscription below the view of the battle are statements, one in English and one in French, of the forces and losses of the two squadrons. ☆ *Rich*^d*. Paton, Pinxit. Lerpiniere & Fittler Sculp*^{nt}*.* ☆ *J. Boydell excudit 1781.* ☆ *Published Dec*^r*. 12*th*. 1780, by John Boydell, Engraver, in Cheapside, London.*

Line engraving. 17¼ in. by 22½ in. Colored by hand. ☆ Parker 78–a.

LENT BY IRVING S. OLDS.

A scratch letter proof of this engraving in black and white is contained in the Beverley R. Robinson Collection. It is inscribed: "The desperate Fight of Captⁿ. Pearson of the Serapis, & Paul Jones, Commander of the Bon Homme Richard, on the 23^d. Day of Septr. 1779. Rich^d. Paton Pinxit. John Boydell Excudit 1781. Daniel Lerpiniere Sculpsit published Jany. 1st 1781 by John Boydell, Engraver in Cheapside London"

17½ in. by 22⅞ in. *Illustrated*

The original painting of this engagement by Richard Paton is now in the Naval Academy Museum at Annapolis, Md.

ENGAGEMENT BETWEEN BON HOMME RICHARD AND SERAPIS, SEPTEMBER 23, 1779   (See No. 5)

Engraved by Daniel Lerpinière after a painting by Richard Paton

Richard Paton (1717–1791) painted a number of British naval actions, which were later made the subjects of engravings published in England. Paton had been early taken to sea by his patron, Admiral Knowles. He thus acquired a first-hand knowledge of ships, which is reflected in the accuracy of his marine paintings. Many of Paton's paintings were currently exhibited at the Royal Academy in London.

Daniel Lerpinière (1740–1790) and James Fittler (1758–1835) were jointly or severally the engravers of numerous English marine prints.

John Boydell (1719–1804) was a well-known and successful London engraver and publisher. He did a great deal to raise the quality of engraving in England to a high level. Boydell was Lord Mayor of London in 1791 and the founder of the Shakespeare Gallery.

6

*To the Merchants trading to Russia, this Print representing the gallant Defence of Capt*ⁿ*. Pearson in his Majesty's Ship Serapis, and the Countess of Scarborough Arm'd Ship Capt*ⁿ*. Piercy, against Paul Jones's Squadron, whereby a valuable Fleet from the Baltic were prevented from falling into the hands of the Enemy, is with the greatest respect Inscribed, by their Humble Servant John Harris.* ☆ Below this inscription is the following description of the engagement: "This desperate Action was fought the 23 Sepʳ. 1779 off Scarborough, The *Serapis* for three hours sustaining a very unequal Fight, having the *Bon Homme Richard* fast locked alongside by the sheet Anchor hooking his Mizen Chains; at the same time the *Alliance* sailing round them pouring in her Broadsides raking her Fore and Aft without their being able to bring a Gun to bear upon her, more than half her people killed & wounded, & several times on Fire, was forced to submit. The *Countess of Scarborough* engaged the *Pallas* but having 7 Guns dismounted, her Sails & Rigging much wrecked she struck to a superior Force." ☆ On the sides are tables of the British and American forces in this battle. Russian coat-of-arms at bottom center. ☆ *Rob*ᵗ*. Dodd, Pinxit. J. Peltro, Fecit.* ☆ *London Publish'd 1 Dec*ʳ*. 1781, by John Harris, Sweetings Alley Cornhill.*

Line engraving. 12 in. by 17¼ in. In black and white. ☆ Parker 78–b.

LENT BY IRVING S. OLDS.

Robert Dodd (1748–1816) was one of the leading and most popular British marine painters of his day. He was also a talented engraver and a publisher of naval prints.

A complete collection of engravings of British naval battles will contain many prints bearing the name of John Peltro (1760–1808) as engraver, or that of John

Harris (1756–1846) as publisher. Peltro was also the engraver of many views of English country homes.

7

Combat memorable entre le Pearson et Paul Jones doné le 22 7bre 1779. le capitaine Pearson comendant le Serapis et Paul Jones commandant le Bon home Richart, et son Escadre. ☆ Similar inscription in German. ☆ *Richard Paton pinxit. Gravé par Balth Frederic Leizelt.* ☆ *Se vend á Augsbourg au Negoce camun de l'Academie Imperiale d'Empire des Arts liberaux avec Privilege de Sa Majeste Imperiale et avec Defense ni d'en faire, ni de vendres les Copies.* ☆ Undated.

Line engraving. 9¾ in. by 14¾ in. Colored by hand. ☆ Published at Augsbourg about 1779 for use in transfer of the print onto glass. The view of the battle is the reverse of that shown in the Paton painting. ☆ Date of the engagement inaccurately stated in the above inscription.

LENT BY IRVING S. OLDS.

8

Combat Mémorable donné le. 22. 7bre. 1779, entre le Capitaine Pearson commandant le Sérapis, et Paul Jones commandant le Bon-Homme Richard et son Escadre. Followed by statement in French of armament, size of crew, and number of casualties on each ship. ☆ Artist and engraver not named. Although not so stated, this print is after the painting by Richard Paton. The view of the battle is also the reverse of that shown in the Paton painting. ☆ *A Paris chez Esnauts et Rapilly, rue St. Jacques a la Ville de Coutances.* ☆ Undated.

Line engraving. 12½ in. by 19⁵⁄₁₆ in. In black and white. ☆ Date of the engagement inaccurately stated in the above inscription.

LENT BY IRVING S. OLDS.

9

Combat Mémorable donné le 22. 7bre. 1779, entre le Captaine Pearson commandant le Sérapis, et Paul Jones commandant le Bon-Homme-Richard et son Escadre. Followed by statement in French of armament, size of crew, and number of casualties of each ship. ☆ Artist and engraver not named. Although not so stated, this print is also after the painting by Richard Paton, with the view reversed. ☆ *A Paris chez Mondhare et Jean rue St. Jean de Beauvais, No. 4.* ☆ Undated.

Line engraving. 12⅜ in. by 19¼ in. In black and white. ☆ Date of the engagement inaccurately stated in the above inscription. ☆ Similar to the foregoing engraving and may be an earlier state of the same print.

LENT BY ESTATE OF FRANCIS P. GARVAN.

IO

Engagement between the Serapis Capt. Pearson, & the Bonne homme Richard, Paul Jones. Commander. ☆ *Engagement between His Majestys Ship the Serapis of 44 guns Captn Pearson & the Bon Homme Rich^d. 40 guns Commanded by Paul Jones which continued upward of 3 hours. both Ships lying so colse fore & aft that the muzzles of their guns touched each Others sides Also between the Scarborough of 26 Guns & Pallas frigates of 32 guns & the Alliance of 36 &c.* Medallion portraits of Sir Rich^d. Pearson and Captn. Paul Jones in upper corners. ☆ Artist and engraver not named. ☆ *London, Published as the Act directs 4th of April 1790 by C. Sheppard, Lambert Hill, Doctors Commons.*

Line engraving. 12⅞ in. by 20 in. In black and white.

LENT BY H. WUNDERLICH AND O. M. TORRINGTON.

II

Paul Jones. Attaque une Flotte Anglaise commandeé par Pearson, revenant de la Baltique en 1793. ☆ *Imp. par Lemercier. Dessiné et lith. par Ferd. Perrot.* ☆ *London—Published by the Anaglyphic Company, 25, Berners St. Oxford St. Paris— publié par V^or. Delarue & Cie. Place du Louvre, 10 Leipzig bei Gebruder Rocca.* ☆ Undated.

Lithograph. 11¼ in. by 16⅞ in. Colored by hand.

LENT BY ESTATE OF FRANCIS P. GARVAN.

IIa

Another lithograph of this same view, of approximately the same size and with the same title, bears the following inscription regarding the lithographer:

Dessiné et Lith. par Ferd. Perrot. Lith. Rigo f^s. et Cie. r. Richer 7. ☆ *Paris, chez Victor Delarue et Cie E 75 Place du Louvre, 10.* ☆ Undated.

Lithograph. 11¼ in. by 16⁵⁄₁₆ in. Colored by hand.

LENT BY HENRY O. HAVEMEYER.

12

Naval Heroes of the United States. No. 3. Bon Homme Richard and Serapis. ☆ Oval portraits of *John Paul Jones, Alexander Murray, Richard Dale, Nicholas Biddle, Edward Preble* and *John Barry* around view of engagement between *Bon*

Homme Richard and *Serapis* in center. ☆ *Lith. & Pub. by N. Currier, 2 Spruce St. N. Y.* ☆ *Entered according to Act of Congress in the year 1846 by N. Currier in the Clerk's office of the District Court of the Southern District of N. Y.*

Lithograph. 9½ in. by 12¾ in. Colored by hand. ☆ H. T. Peters's Currier & Ives 1938.

LENT BY IRVING S. OLDS.

NATHANIEL CURRIER (1813–1888) is the best known of early American lithographers. He was born in Roxbury, Mass. After serving an apprenticeship with the Pendleton brothers in Boston, Currier went first to Philadelphia and then to New York in 1834, where he took up lithography as a profession. By 1835 Currier had an independent business and was issuing prints under his own name. In 1857, Currier formed with J. M. Ives the famous firm of Currier & Ives, which over the many years of its existence rightfully earned for itself the reputation of *Print-Makers to the American People.*

13

The Engagement of Captn. Pearson in His Majesty's Ship Serapis, with Paul Jones of the American Ship of War called the Bon Homme Richard: in which Action the former was taken, while the Countess of Scarborough was also captured by the Pallas frigate. ☆ *Drawn by Hamilton.* ☆ *Engraved by R. Collier.* ☆ *Engraved for Barnard's New Complete & Authentic History of England.*

Line engraving. 10⅝ in. by 7 in., including engraved borders. Printed in colors. ☆ The first edition of Barnard's *History of England* was published in England in 1782.

LENT BY IRVING S. OLDS.

14

The Action Between The Serapis And Bon Homme Richard Septr. 23rd. 1779. ☆ *Painted by James Hamilton.* ☆ *Engraved by R. Whitechurch.* ☆ *Published by Fishel, Adler & Schwartz, New York Fishel, Adler & Co. New York & Berlin.* ☆ Mixed engraving. 21⅜ in. by 32⅜ in. Colored by hand.

LENT BY BEVERLEY R. ROBINSON.

A proof of this engraving before letters is known.

PART II

QUASI-WAR WITH FRANCE

CONSTELLATION AND L'INSURGENTE

FEBRUARY 9, 1799

This engagement was undoubtedly the most outstanding in our so-called quasi-war with France, lasting from 1798 to 1801.

Following the conclusion of the Revolutionary War, the export trade of the United States grew by leaps and bounds. During the last decade of the eighteenth century, American sailing vessels were a common sight in most of the important harbors of the world. The gigantic struggle between England and France, commencing anew in 1793, gave our merchants an opportunity to take over a large part of the ocean-borne commerce formerly carried by the ships of these two nations. Despite our neutrality in the Anglo-French war, the sailing ships of the United States became the prey of French privateers. No navy then existed to protect our shipping.

Official relations between the two democracies were unsatisfactory. President Washington toward the end of his second term found it necessary to ask for the recall of Citizen Genet, the first Minister to the United States from the new Republic of France. Early in the presidency of John Adams, the French Directory treated with insolence the envoys sent to France by the President. French interference with our commerce continued.

The situation became so serious that in 1798 a Navy Department was created under Secretary Benjamin Stoddert. Steps were at once taken to speed the completion of the three frigates then being built, and to construct and purchase additional ships of war. When these units of the American Navy took to sea, orders were given to convoy and protect American merchant ships, and in these operations to engage both French privateers and French men-of-war, although there had been no formal declaration of war against France.

Commodore Thomas Truxton in the new frigate *Constellation*, 36 guns, after a chase, encountered the French frigate *L'Insurgente*, 36 guns, off the

Island of St. Christopher in the West Indies on February 9, 1799. After a hard-fought engagement of more than an hour in a rough sea, in which Commodore Truxton reported that he got his ship "in a position for every shot to do execution," Captain Barreaut of the frigate *L'Insurgente* struck his colors.

This victory demonstrated the sturdy quality of the new units of the American Navy and also the effective marksmanship of the American gunners. The captured ship was later refitted and sent out as an American man-of-war.

15

Constellation & L'Insurgent—the Chace. ☆ *Painted & Engraved by E. Savage. Philad^a. Published by E. Savage May 20th. 1799.*

Aquatint. 13½ in. by 20⅞ in. In black and white. ☆ Stauffer 2758.   *Illustrated*

16

Action between the Constellation and L'Insurgent,—On the 9th. February 1799.— Off the Island of S^t. Christophers, when after an hard fought battle of one hour and a quarter the Frigate of the Directory yielded to superior skill and bravery. Killed on board L'Insurgent 29. Wounded 46. Constellation 1 killed, 3 wounded. Force of the Constellation Guns 36. Men 310. Force of the Insurgent 40 Guns 18 Brass Swivels 409 Men ☆ *Painted & Engraved by E. Savage.* ☆ *Philad^a. Published by E. Savage, May 20 1799.*

Aquatint. 13¾ in. by 20⅛ in. In black and white. Companion piece to the foregoing. ☆ Stauffer 2757.

ABOVE PAIR OF AQUATINTS LENT BY VALENTINE HOLLINGSWORTH.

These two prints are believed to be the earliest aquatints of a naval engagement by an American-born engraver.

EDWARD SAVAGE (1761–1817) was born in Massachusetts, became a portrait painter, studied mezzotint and stipple engraving in London, and subsequently settled in Philadelphia, where he engraved a number of important portraits. Probably the best known of his paintings and engravings are those of George Washington.

(CONSTELLATION & L'INSURGENT~ the CHACE.)

THE CHASE OF L'INSURGENTE BY THE CONSTELLATION, FEBRUARY 9, 1799

Painted and engraved by Edward Savage

(See No. 15)

Truxton's Victory. Engagement between the United States Frigate Constellation of 36 Guns, Commanded by Capt. Truxton, and L'Insurgente French Frigate of 40 Guns, Capt. Bureaut Feby. 9th 1799. ☆ Published and Sold by E. Pember and S. Luzerder, Philadelphia. ☆ Artist and engraver not named. Undated.

An engraving of Washington is printed on the reverse side.

Line engraving. 8³⁄₁₆ in. by 11 in. In black and white. ☆ Fielding 1925.

LENT BY ESTATE OF FRANCIS P. GARVAN.

18

A View of the American Frigate, Constellation, capturing the French National Frigate, L'Insurgente, within sight of Basseterre. Feby. 9th 1799. The Ships commenced a running fight near Nevis, and afterwards continued in close Action for three quarters of an hour, when the French Frigate was compelled to strike her Colours to the Victorious Americans. Statement of armament and losses of each ship follows. ☆ Artist and engraver not named. ☆ *Publish'd Octr. 1st. 1800 by John Fairburn 146 Minories London.*

Stipple and line engraving. 8⅞ in. by 13⅝ in. Colored by hand.

LENT BY THE FRANKLIN D. ROOSEVELT LIBRARY, HYDE PARK, N. Y.

PART III

WAR WITH TRIPOLI

WAR WITH TRIPOLI
1801–1805

The pirates of the four Barbary States in North Africa (Algiers, Morocco, Tripoli and Tunis) found to their liking the vast development of American shipping which followed not long after the Revolutionary War had ended. They captured and plundered American merchant ships in both the Mediterranean Sea and the Atlantic Ocean. The last vessel of the Continental Navy had been sold in 1785. Accordingly, American merchant ships for some years thereafter had to depend upon their own armament for protection.

In 1794 Congress authorized the building of six frigates (work thereon to cease in the event of a treaty with Algiers) in order to combat this menace to continued American commercial prosperity, deciding that such a course was preferable to the payment of tribute. A disadvantageous peace was concluded with Algiers in 1796. Upon the urgent appeal of President Washington, Congress permitted work on three of the frigates to go forward, which was speeded in 1798, when called for by the then serious state of our relations with France. The construction or purchase of additional men-of-war was also authorized at that time.

This was the real beginning of the Navy of the United States of America. The first three ships completed were the frigates *Constellation*, *United States* and *Constitution*, all of which were destined to achieve fame in subsequent sea battles.

After truces of a sort had been negotiated with Morocco, Algiers, Tunis and Tripoli, the Pasha of Tripoli in 1801 demanded a new treaty with the United States upon exorbitant terms, and ended by declaring war on May 10, 1801.

An American fleet was soon sent out to the Mediterranean to blockade Tripoli. This squadron was successively commanded by Commodores Richard

Dale, Richard Morris, Edward Preble, Samuel Barron and John Rodgers. Such a fleet remained in the Mediterranean until after a satisfactory treaty of peace was signed with Tripoli on June 10, 1805.

The most spectacular incidents of the War with Tripoli concerned the frigate *Philadelphia* and the ketch *Intrepid*. On October 31, 1803, the *Philadelphia*, commanded by Captain William Bainbridge, had the misfortune to run on an uncharted reef after chasing a Tripolitan cruiser near the harbor of Tripoli. When a strenuous effort to refloat the vessel failed, Captain Bainbridge was forced to surrender to the enemy gunboats which had come out from Tripoli to attack the *Philadelphia* in her defenseless condition. Later on, the Tripolitans succeeded in freeing the American frigate and took her into the inner harbor of Tripoli.

Operation by the Tripolitans of such a powerful ship as the *Philadelphia* would be of distinct disadvantage to the American Mediterranean squadron. So plans were laid by Commodore Preble for the destruction of the captured frigate.

Eighty-four volunteers, under the leadership of Lieutenant Stephen Decatur, sailed into the harbor of Tripoli on the night of February 16, 1804, on board the ketch *Intrepid*, a renamed captured vessel of Mediterranean rig. The guard on the *Philadelphia*, believing the story of the *Intrepid's* pilot that she was a ship from Malta recently purchased by Tripoli, actually assisted in tying the *Intrepid* up to the *Philadelphia*. The truth was not discovered until Decatur and his men were ready to board the former American frigate. They soon overcame the Tripolitans, set fire to and destroyed the *Philadelphia* in accordance with their plan, escaping on the *Intrepid*, only one man being slightly injured. Among the members of this brave group were James Lawrence and Thomas Macdonough, later to become outstanding naval commanders in the War of 1812.

On August 3, 1804, the American squadron, under Commodore Edward Preble, which then included the frigate *Constitution* as flagship, attacked the town of Tripoli and engaged the considerable Tripolitan naval force in the harbor. At the end of the day's fight, three of the enemy's ships had been sunk, three more captured, and serious damage done to the town and its shore batteries. This was the first of five general bombardments of Tripoli during

August and September 1804. The offensive strength of the American naval force was the principal factor which brought about the eventual peace with Tripoli.

The *Intrepid* later figured in another daring exploit, which ended disastrously. Converted into a fire-ship, loaded with powder and shells, she was taken into the harbor of Tripoli on the night of September 4, 1804, with a view to having her cargo exploded in the midst of the Tripolitan naval and other craft at anchor in the port. This time her crew of volunteers was thirteen in number, commanded by Master Commandant Richard Somers and assisted by Lieutenants Wadsworth and Israel. Unfortunately, the *Intrepid* was discovered and boarded before the program could be effected. The magazine of the *Intrepid* was exploded, and all on board, both Americans and Tripolitans, lost their lives.

19

Capt. Sterrett in the Sch^r. Enterprise paying tribute to Tripoli, August 1801. ☆ *M. Cornè, p.* ☆ Engraver and publisher not named. ☆ Undated.

Line engraving. 3⅜ in. by 6¹¹⁄₁₆ in. Colored by hand.

LENT BY ESTATE OF FRANCIS P. GARVAN.

20

A perspective View of the loss of the U. S. Frigate Philadelphia in which is represented her relative position to the Tripolitan Gun-boats when during their furious attack upon her she was unable to get a single gun to bear upon them. ☆ *Ch^s. Denoon del:* ☆ Undated.

Line engraving. 11⅜ in. by 19+ in. Colored by hand.

LENT BY FRANKLIN D. ROOSEVELT.

This rare print is from the Collection of President Roosevelt at The White House.

According to the records of the Navy Department, Charles Denoon or Dinoon was a seaman on board the U. S. Frigate *Philadelphia* at the time of her loss. Presumably, Denoon was a prisoner of war at Tripoli during the balance of the Tripolitan War.

The U. S. Frigate Philadelphia on the Rocks Off Tripoli Oct. 31ˢᵗ 1801. ☆ P. S. Duval, Lith. Philᵃ. On Stone by E. J. Pinkerton. ☆ U. S. Military Magazine, Army & Navy. Vol. 2ⁿᵈ.

Lithograph. 7¼ in. by 10⅞ in. Colored by hand. ☆ Date of this disaster inaccurately stated. ☆ Published by Huddy & Duval, Philadelphia, November 1840.

LENT BY HENRY O. HAVEMEYER.

22

Burning of the Frigate Philadelphia in the Harbour of Tripoli, 16ᵗʰ Feb. 1804, by 70 Gallant Tars of Columbia commanded by Lieut. Decatur. ☆ Engraved & Published by F. Kearny, 34 Liberty Street, N. Y. August 1. 1808. Printed by A Maverick. ☆ Undated.

Aquatint. 12⅞ in. by 17⅞ in. Colored by hand.

LENT BY ESTATE OF FRANCIS P. GARVAN.

A similar aquatint of the same size and with the same title was also issued, presumably contemporaneously, but without naming the artist, engraver, publisher, or date of publication.

FRANCIS KEARNY (circa 1780–1833) was a well-known American engraver, first carrying on an engraving business in New York and later in Philadelphia from about 1810 to 1833. He is said to have learned drawing with Archibald and Alexander Robertson and engraving with Peter R. Maverick in New York. Kearny also published prints at Philadelphia.

ANDREW MAVERICK, a son of the early New York engraver, Peter Rushton Maverick, conducted a print publishing business at New York.

23

Nautical Exploit, Dedicated to Commodore Ed. Preble, and the Gallant Tars, of the Infant American Navy. ☆ The American Ketch Intrepid of 4 guns and 70 men, commanded by Lieutenant Decatur, boarding and burning the Tripolitan Frigate (late the Philadelphia) in the middle of the harbour of Tripoli, close to the batteries, and within musket shot of two Corsairs, full of men, on the night of the 16ᵗʰ. of February 1804. ☆ L. Binsse delᵗ. Aubertin, sculpᵗ. ☆ Undated.

Aquatint. 17¼ in. by 21½ in. Colored by hand.

LENT BY IRVING S. OLDS.

24

The burning of the American Frigate the Philadelphia in the Harbour of Tripoli happily executed by the valiant Cap: Decatur to whom this Plate is respectfully dedicated by his Obedient Servant John B. Guerrazzi. ☆ *Sold in Leghorn 1805.*

Line engraving. 11¼ in. by 15½ in. In black and white.

LENT BY DR. EUGENE H. POOL.

25

Burning of the Philadelphia in the Harbor of Tripoli (in pencil) *William Hamlin Sc.* ☆ Proof before letters. ☆ Undated.

Mezzotint. 2⅜ in. by 3¹¹⁄₁₆ in. In black and white. ☆ Believed to have been intended as an illustration for the *Life of General Eaton.* ☆ Stauffer 1247.

LENT BY HALL PARK McCULLOUGH.

WILLIAM HAMLIN (1772–1869) was born in Providence, R. I., where he first entered business as a manufacturer and repairer of sextants and other nautical instruments. Engraving upon metal as a part of his regular duties led to copperplate engraving, and before long Hamlin was established in business as an engraver. Hamlin made several engraved portraits of Washington and did a number of book illustrations.

26

The attack made on Tripoli on the 3ᵈ. August 1804. by the American Squadron under Comodore Edward Preble to whom this Plate is respectfully dedicated by his Obedient Servant John B. Guerrazzi. ☆ *Sold in Leghorn 1805.*

Line engraving. 11⅝ in. by 15¾ in. In sepia.

LENT BY IRVING S. OLDS.

27

A View of Commodore Preble's Squadron whilst engaging the Gun-boats and Forts of Tropoli on the 3ʳᵈ. of August 1804. when they captured three of the Tripolitan Gun-boats & greatly damag'd the Bashaw's Fortifications. Followed by a list of the ships, forts, etc. depicted in the engraving. ☆ *Chˢ. Denoon delᵗ.* ☆ Undated.

Line engraving. 11⅜ in. by 19+ in. Colored by hand.   *Illustrated*

LENT BY FRANKLIN D. ROOSEVELT.

This rare print is from the Collection of President Roosevelt at The White House.

COMMODORE PREBLE'S ATTACK ON TRIPOLI, AUGUST 3, 1804

Engraved by Charles Denoon

(See No. 27)

CHARLES DENOON, a seaman on board the U. S. Frigate *Philadelphia* when she was captured by the Tripolitans was probably a prisoner of war at Tripoli at the time of Commodore Preble's attack against that fortress on August 3, 1804.

28

August 1804. Bombardment of Tripoli. ☆ *Lith. & Pub. by N. Currier 2 Spruce St. N. Y.* ☆ *Entered according to Act of Congress in the year 1846 by N. Currier, in the Clerk's office of the District Court of the Southern District of N. Y.*

Lithograph. 7⅞ in. by 12⅞ in. Colored by hand. ☆ H. T. Peters's Currier & Ives 1176.

LENT BY IRVING S. OLDS.

29

Blowing Up of the Fire Ship Intrepid commanded by Capt. Somers in the Harbour of Tripoli on the night of the 4th. Sepr. 1804. ☆ Below this title is the following description of the exploit: "Before the *Intrepid* had gained her Destined situation she was suddenly boarded by 100 Tripolines, when the Gallant Somers and Heroes of his Party. (Lieut^ts. Wadsworth and Israel and 10 Men.) observed themselves surrounded by 3 Gun-boats, and no prospect of Escape, determined at once to prefer Death and the Destruction of the Enemy, to Captivity & a torturing Slavery, put a Match to train leading directly to the Magazines, which at once blew the whole into the Air." Various places in the harbor are named directly under the engraved view. ☆ Engraver, artist and publisher not named. ☆ Undated.

Line engraving. 9⅞ in. by 14 in. In black and white.

LENT BY HENRY O. HAVEMEYER.

PART IV

PRESIDENT AND LITTLE BELT EPISODE

PRESIDENT AND LITTLE BELT
MAY 15, 1811

The outbreak of general war in Europe in 1793 caused the belligerents to attempt to prevent supplies reaching the enemy through neutral shipping. The United States, as the then most important neutral commercial nation, was the principal victim of this practice.

For a number of years both England and France sought to impose illegal restraints upon our ocean shipping and seriously interfered therewith. Great feeling against England was aroused in this country on this score, and also on account of that nation's oft-repeated impressment of American sailors to serve in the British Navy. Ships of the Royal Navy frequently intercepted our merchant vessels on the high seas—on two occasions even American men-of-war—and forcibly removed therefrom seamen of British birth, even though they had later become naturalized citizens of the United States.

On the evening of May 15, 1811, Commodore John Rodgers, who had been sent out in the frigate *President* to protect our sea lanes to the West Indies, encountered the British sloop-of-war *Little Belt*, Captain Arthur B. Bingham, off Cape Henry on the Virginia coast. After a quarter of an hour of fighting, during which the smaller *Little Belt* sustained considerable damage, her British identity became known and further firing ceased. England and the United States were then nominally at peace. On the following day Commodore Rodgers expressed to Captain Bingham of the *Little Belt* his regret over the unfortunate affair.

In a subsequent inquiry, in which Commodore Rodgers was absolved from blame, there was evidence that the *Little Belt* had fired the first and the last shots. The official orders to Commodore Rodgers referred to the British impressment of sailors from the American frigate *Chesapeake* in her encounter with the British ship *Leopard* a few years before, and set forth that the American commander was to "maintain and support at every risk and cost the dignity of our flag."

[27]

30

The Little Belt, Sloop of War, Cap^{tn}. Bingham nobly supporting the Honor of the British Flag, against the President United States Frigate, Commodore Rogers, May 15th. 1811. ☆ W^{m}. Elmes del^{t}. W^{m}. Elmes sculp^{s}. ☆ Pub'd & Sold Octr. 25. 1811, by Edwd. Orme Printseller to his Majesty & Royal Family, Engraver & Publisher, Bond St. Corner of Brook St. London.

Aquatint. 14⅜ in. by 19¼ in. Colored by hand.

LENT BY ESTATE OF FRANCIS P. GARVAN.

EDWARD ORME was publisher to the King of England and to the Prince Regent. He was the publisher of Orme's *Historic Military and Naval Anecdotes.*

31

To The Right Honorable Charles Philip Yorke, First Lord of the Admiralty, This Print elucidating the extreme disproportion of Force between the American Frigate President Commodore Rodgers, and His Majesty's Sloop the Little Belt Arthur Butt Bingham Esquire Commander, and representing the situation of both Ships in the morning after the Action of the 11 May 1811, is respectfully inscribed by his obliged Servant Jos^{h}. Cartwright. Description of armament and size of crew of two ships follows. ☆ Drawn by J. Cartwright. Engraved by J. Hassell. ☆ London, Pub. 1 Dec. 1811 by J. Hassell, N°. 11 Clements Inn, & J. Cartwright, 39. Arundel Street, Strand.

Aquatint. 13⅞ in. by 20¼ in. Colored by hand. ☆ Parker 213–b.

LENT BY ESTATE OF FRANCIS P. GARVAN.

32

The American Frigate President Commodore Rogers, engaging the little Belt Captn. Bingham. ☆ Printed & Published by Langley & Belch N°. 173 High S^{t}. Borough London. ☆ Artist and engraver not named. ☆ Undated.

Pair of stipple and line engravings, printed on same sheet, upper one being in outline form. 4⅞ in. by 7⅛ in., each. In black and white. ☆ Parker 213–a.

LENT BY HENRY O. HAVEMEYER.

33

The American Frigate President Commodore Rogers, engaging the little Belt Captn. Bingham. ☆ Printed & Sold by W. Belch, N^{o}.: 258 High Street, Borough London. ☆ Artist and engraver not named. ☆ Undated.

Stipple and line engraving. 4⅞ in. by 7³⁄₁₆ in. Colored by hand.

LENT BY HENRY O. HAVEMEYER.

PART V

WAR OF 1812

ESCAPE OF THE BELVIDERA
FROM THE PRESIDENT
JUNE 23, 1812

On June 18, 1812, a state of war was declared to exist with Great Britain. "Free Trade and Sailors' Rights" and "On to Canada" became our national slogans. At sea, the odds were tremendously in favor of England, except that her main concern in 1812 was the great pending struggle with Napoleon.

The United States Navy at the beginning of the war comprised only sixteen available vessels, a relatively insignificant force with which to oppose the mighty Royal Navy of more than six hundred units. Three or four squadrons of the British navy were then in the waters of the Western Hemisphere, a few ships being in the immediate vicinity of our coast.

Three days after war was declared, an American squadron of five vessels under the command of Commodore John Rodgers set sail from New York to protect American ships at sea and to capture or destroy a homeward bound British plate fleet from Jamaica.

On June 23, 1812, the *President*, Commodore Rodgers's flagship of 44 guns, came upon the British frigate *Belvidera* of 36 guns, Captain Richard Byron. A running fight ensued, from which the *Belvidera* eventually escaped by throwing overboard her small boats, anchors and spare spars and by pumping out a large part of her supply of fresh water. Early in the engagement, the *President* was handicapped by the explosion of a main-deck gun, which damaged the ship and killed or wounded sixteen of the crew, including Commodore Rodgers, whose leg was broken.

After the escape of the *Belvidera*, the American squadron continued its cruise, which lasted ninety days and took the ships close to the English Channel and then to Boston. Only seven prizes were taken, the British plate fleet from Jamaica being missed.

34

Combat soutenu le 23 Aout 1812 par la Frégate le President, des Etats-Unis d'Amerique, et la Frégate Anglaise le Belvédere ☆ Litho: de Auger. ☆ Undated.

Lithograph. 7¼ in. by 11⅜ in. Colored by hand.

LENT BY ESTATE OF FRANCIS P. GARVAN.

ESCAPE OF THE CONSTITUTION
JULY 17–19, 1812

At the outbreak of the war, the frigate *Constitution*, 44 guns, Captain Isaac Hull, was at Annapolis. On July 17, 1812, the *Constitution*, while off the New Jersey coast, en route from Annapolis to New York to avoid the possibility of being blockaded in Chesapeake Bay, found herself in the immediate neighborhood of a powerful British squadron, consisting of a ship of the line, four frigates, and two smaller vessels, commanded by Captain Philip B. V. Broke.

Captain Hull, with the able assistance of Lieutenant Charles Morris, kept his ship out of effective range of the British guns by most skillful handling, the *Constitution* in the light wind being carried forward at times through being towed by her own small boats and by kedging. This chase continued for the greater part of three days and nights when the *Constitution* finally ran into a favorable breeze and escaped, reaching Boston safely on July 26, 1812.

35

Constitution's Escape from the British Squadron after a chase of sixty hours. Names of the various ships indicated below the view. ☆ M. Cornè p.   W. Hoogland Sc. ☆ Engraved for The Naval Monument. ☆ Entered according to Act of Congress Nov. 25, 1815 by A. Bowen.

Line engraving. 3¹⁵⁄₁₆ in. by 7⅞ in. In black and white. ☆ Stauffer 1436.

LENT BY HENRY O. HAVEMEYER.

WILLIAM HOOGLAND established himself as an engraver in New York and later in Boston. His work was in both stipple and line engraving. He was one of the early American banknote engravers.

ABEL BOWEN (1790–1850) was an engraver and printer at Boston. In 1816, he published *The Naval Monument*, containing accounts of the naval battles between the United States and England during the War of 1812. This book was illustrated by numerous copper and woodcut views of American naval engagements, many engraved by Bowen himself. In 1825, Bowen published Shaw's *History of Boston*, for which he engraved some full-page views. His line engraving of the U. S. Frigate *Constitution*, separately published, is a highly prized item. It is included in this exhibition as No. 214, and is reproduced on the cover of this publication.

35 a

A contemporaneous water color painting of this famous exploit of the U. S. Frigate *Constitution* is included in this exhibition. It is inscribed by hand: "The Constitution escaping the British Fleet July 17, 1812. Jos. Rouillard pinxit 1813." ☆ 10⅛ in. by 17⅜ in.

LENT BY HALL PARK McCULLOUGH.

ESSEX AND ALERT
AUGUST 13, 1812

This was the first American victory at sea over a British man-of-war during the War of 1812. Fifteen days after the declaration of war, Captain David Porter in command of the frigate *Essex*, 32 guns, sailed from New York. He took a course to the south in search of a British frigate carrying specie for South America.

On August 13, 1812, the *Essex* came on the British sloop-of-war *Alert*, 16 guns, in the vicinity of the West Indies. The *Essex* assumed the appearance of a merchantman endeavoring to escape. The British ship dispensed with the customary maneuvers and sought out the American frigate. The action is best described in the following excerpt from the official report of Captain Porter: "His Britannic Majesty's sloop-of-war *Alert*, Capt. T. L. P. Laugharne, ran down on our weather quarter, gave three cheers, and commenced an action (if so trifling a skirmish deserves the name) and after eight minutes firing struck her colors, with seven feet water in her hold, much cut to pieces, and 3 men wounded . . . The *Essex* has not received the slightest injury. The *Alert* was out for the purpose of taking the *Hornet*."

When Captain Porter returned to New York in September 1812, the *Essex* had taken ten prizes.

A small vignette of the action between the *Essex* and the *Alert* is contained on *An Improved Map of the United States* by Shelton & Kensett (No. 216 in this exhibition). An engraving of the engagement will be found in the print of various naval actions (No. 220 in this exhibition).

CONSTITUTION AND GUERRIÈRE

AUGUST 19, 1812

The nation was swept by a wave of patriotism, enthusiasm and rejoicing when news came of this victory at sea in our first real engagement of the War of 1812. Two frigates of somewhat equal strength had met, and, after a skillfully fought action, the British ship had been reduced to a helpless hulk, with relatively small American losses.

Shortly after the escape of the *Constitution* from a mighty British squadron off New York, the *Guerrière* being one of this pursuing fleet, Captain Isaac Hull and his ship set sail from Boston early in August 1812 on a solitary expedition in the hope of harassing the enemy's shipping or of encountering a British man-of-war. A cruise to the Bay of Fundy and the mouth of the Gulf of St. Lawrence brought a few unimportant prizes.

While southward bound, the *Constitution* sighted the *Guerrière*, 38 guns, commanded by Captain James R. Dacres, southeast of Halifax on the afternoon of August 19, 1812. Both ships got into position and made ready for an engagement. By 6 P.M., following able maneuvering, the vessels were alongside and then engaged in broadside fire at close range. After fifteen minutes of such fighting, the mizzen-mast of the *Guerrière* was hit and fell overboard. When the rigging of the ships became entangled, Captain Hull prepared to board. The two frigates soon fell apart, and boarding was made unnecessary by the crashing of the two remaining masts of the British frigate. The *Guerrière*, now a badly damaged and helpless hulk, struck her colors at 6:30 P.M.

Seventy-nine of the British crew had been killed or wounded, the American losses being seven killed and an equal number wounded. Captain Hull took his prisoners on board the *Constitution* and burned the *Guerrière*, whose cut-up condition did not warrant any attempt to salvage the vessel.

The capture of the *Guerrière* was a much needed fillip to the morale of the country, then at a low ebb following the disastrous failure of the land operations in the vicinity of Detroit. Captain Hull's victory was of great importance in establishing respect for the fighting ability of both the frigates of the tiny United States Navy and their officers and men.

36

This Representation of the U. S. Frigate Constitution, Isaac Hull, Esqr. Commander, Capturing His Britannic Majesty's Frigate Guerriere, James R. Dacres Esqr. Commander; Is respectfully inscribed to Capt. Isaac Hull, his Officers and Gallant Crew; by their devoted humble Servant, James Webster. Fought August 19, 1812. ☆ Detailed description of the engagement at the bottom of the print. Small bust portrait of Captain Hull, engraved by David Edwin, at center of bottom margin, with the heading "Veni, Vidi, Vici". ☆ *The Constitution had 7 men killed & 7 wounded. The Guerriere had 15 men killed & 63 wounded.* ☆ *Painted by T. Birch, A. C. S. A.* ☆ *Engraved by C. Tiebout, A. C. S. A.* ☆ *Subscription Price $5.00.* ☆ *Entered according to Act of Congress the 18th. day of August 1813 by James Webster of State of Pennsylvania.*

Stipple engraving. 17¾ in. by 26⅜ in. Colored by hand. Stauffer 3206.

LENT BY HARRY S. NEWMAN. *Illustrated*

Companion piece to the print of the action between the *United States* and the *Macedonian*, engraved by S. Seymour after the painting by T. Birch.

THOMAS BIRCH (circa 1779–1851), a son of William Birch, the engraver, painted a number of well-known representations of naval engagements of the War of 1812. He was born in London. As a youth he came to Pennsylvania with his father, settling in Philadelphia about 1800. He probably assisted his father in the production of the plates for Birch's *Views of Philadelphia*, issued in 1800 under the name of W. Birch & Son. Thomas Birch first took up portrait painting, but after 1807 devoted his efforts to marine painting and in this work established an enviable reputation for himself.

CORNELIUS TIEBOUT (circa 1777–1830) is described by Stauffer as "the first American-born professional engraver to produce really meritorious work." He was descended from an American Huguenot family, and was probably born in New York City, where as a young man he learned to engrave upon metal as an apprentice to a silversmith. In 1793 Tiebout went to London and learned the art

ENGAGEMENT BETWEEN CONSTITUTION AND GUERRIÈRE, AUGUST 19, 1812 (See No. 36)

Engraved by Cornelius Tiebout after a painting by Thomas Birch

of stipple engraving. Tiebout published in London in 1796 an excellent engraved portrait of John Jay. He returned to New York about that year, and engaged with his brother in the engraving and publishing of prints. Later, Tiebout went to Philadelphia, where for many years he conducted an extensive engraving business. His best known engravings are of an historical character. Tiebout died in Kentucky about 1830.

37

This representation of the engagement between the United States Frigate Constitution, and his Britannic Majesty's Frigate Guerriere; which issued in the Capture and destruction of the Guerriere, on the 19th. of August 1812, is respectfully dedicated to the President of the United States, by the publishers Freeman and Pierie. Time of Action, 30 minutes. Statement of losses of each ship follows. ☆ *Freeman excudit. Engraved from Original Drawings furnished by Capt. I. Hull.* ☆ *Published at Philadelphia & Entered according to Act of Congress, the 8th day of March— 1813, by Freeman & Pierie of the State of Pennsylvania.*

Mezzotint. 15 ⅞ in. by 23 ¾ in. Colored by hand. ☆ This print has been attributed to George Graham, although definitely not so established. ☆ Fielding 1805.

LENT BY ESTATE OF FRANCIS P. GARVAN.

T. W. FREEMAN was a print publisher at Philadelphia, who seems also to have done some engraving. At the time of the isuance of this print in 1813, he was engaged in the publishing business at Philadelphia with J. Pierie.

38

Brilliant Naval Victory, With the U. States Frigate Constitution of 44 Guns, Capn. Hull, & the English Frigate Guerriere of 38 Guns, Capn. D'acres, in which action Capn. Hull lost 7 men killed, & 7 wounded, & his B.Ms. Ship was sunk; besides her loss of 15 men killed, 62 wounded, & 24 missing; August 20, 1812. After closing, the action was 30 minus. ☆ *S. Seymour delin sculp.* ☆ *Philadelphia. Published by J. Pierie & F. Kearney 1812.*

Line engraving. 11 ¾ in. by 16 ⅝ in. Colored by hand. Fielding 1428.

LENT BY IRVING S. OLDS.

SAMUEL SEYMOUR was an established and highly regarded engraver, who worked at his profession in Philadelphia from about 1797 to 1822. He engraved a number of portraits, city and rural views, and representations of naval engagements, as well as encyclopedia plates and general book illustrations.

39

Engagement between the U. S. Frigate Constitution Captⁿ. Isaac Hull, & the British Frigate Guerriere, Captⁿ. James R. Dacres, Thursday 19th. August 1812. Extracts from Captⁿ. Hull's Letters, &c. and a statement of the armament and losses of each ship follow. ☆ Published Octr. 1st. 1812, by B. Tanner N°. 74 South 8th. S^t. Philadelphia.

Line engraving. 9⅜ in. by 14⅝ in. Colored by hand. One of a set of two prints. ☆ Fielding 1544.

LENT BY IRVING S. OLDS.

40

Explosion of the British Frigate, Guerriere, James R. Dacres, Esqr. Captⁿ. and Rescue of the Prisoners, &c. the day after her Capture by the U.S. Frigate Constitution, Isaac Hull, Esqr. Comm^r. Friday 20th. Augus^t. 1812. With extracts from Captⁿ. Hull's Letters. ☆ J. J. Barralet Del^t. B. Tanner Sculp^t. ☆ Published Novr. 10th 1812 by B. Tanner N°. 74 South 8th S^t. Phil^a.

Line engraving. 9⅜ in. by 14¾ in. Colored by hand. Companion piece to the foregoing. ☆ Fielding 1545.

LENT BY H. WUNDERLICH AND O. M. TORRINGTON.

A later state of this print omits the names of J. J. Barralet and B. Tanner, and has a publication line reading: *Published Novr. 10th. 1813 by Cammeyer & Acock Libr^y. S^t. Phil^a.*

JOHN JAMES BARRALET was born in Ireland of French parentage around 1747. About 1796 he came to Philadelphia, where he painted portraits and landscapes in water-colors and designed work for other engravers. He engraved a few plates himself and for a time carried on an engraving business in Philadelphia in association with Alexander Lawson. Several well known representations of American naval engagements were painted by Barralet. He died at Philadelphia in 1815.

BENJAMIN TANNER (1775–1848) has a well established reputation as an engraver of American historical subjects. He was born in New York, where he commenced his engraving career, perhaps as a pupil of Peter R. Maverick. Later Tanner carried on business in Philadelphia from about 1805 to 1845 as a general engraver and map and print publisher, first with his brother and subsequently as a member of the engraving firm of Tanner, Vallance, Kearny & Co. Toward the end of his life, Tanner moved to Baltimore, where he died.

41

Signal Naval Victory   Achieved by Capt. Hull, of the U. S. Frigate Constitution, over H. B. Majesty's Frigate Guerriere Capt. Dacres; which terminated in the total destruction of the Enemy's ship, after a close Action of 30 Minutes. Engagement took place Augt. 19 1812, at 6 O'Clock P.M. Statement of armament and losses of each ship follows. ☆ Design'd Engrav'd & Publish'd by W. Strickland & W. Kneass Philad^a. 21^t. Sept. 1812.

Line engraving. 9^{13}⁄$_{16}$ in. by 13^{13}⁄$_{16}$ in. Colored by hand. ☆ Stauffer 1660.

LENT BY ESTATE OF FRANCIS P. GARVAN.

WILLIAM STRICKLAND (1787–1854) was born in Philadelphia, where he studied architecture. When a young man, he took up painting, designing for other engravers, and engraving in aquatint himself. He was one of the earliest American aquatinters. Strickland produced a number of engravings illustrating events in the War of 1812. Later on, Strickland resumed practice as an architect and designed some notable buildings in Philadelphia and elsewhere, including the State House at Nashville, Tenn., where he is buried under the capitol building designed by him.

WILLIAM KNEASS (1781–1840) was born in Lancaster, Pa. He conducted an engraving business at Philadelphia from 1805 up to the time of his death. He was a member of the firm of Kneass & Dellaker, and later of Young, Kneass & Co., general engravers. In 1824, Kneass was appointed engraver and die-sinker at the U. S. Mint in Philadelphia.

42

The U. S. frigate Constitution Commanded by Isaac Hull Esqr. Captured his B. M. frigate Guerriere Capt. Dacres On the 19th. of August 1812. In 30 Minutes (inscribed on a ribbon held by an eagle) ☆ Des^d. Eng^d. & Pub^d. by T. Gimbrede, 19th. Sept. N. Y.

Stipple engraving. 6^1⁄$_8$ in. by 9^9⁄$_{16}$ in. Colored by hand. ☆ First State. Fielding 513i.

LENT BY PEABODY MUSEUM, SALEM, MASS.

THOMAS GIMBREDE (1781–1832) was born in France. He came to this country in 1802 as a painter of miniatures. He took up engraving in New York and produced some excellent portraits, as well as considerable work for the Philadelphia publications *The Port Folio* and *The Analectic Magazine*. In 1819, Gimbrede was appointed drawing master at the U. S. Military Academy at West Point and continued in that position until his death. Gimbrede was a brother-in-law of the well-known engraver, J. F. E. Prud'homme.

43

The U. S. frigate Constitution Commanded by Isaac Hull, Esqr. Captured his B.M. frigate, Guerriere Capt. Dacres in 30 Minutes On the 19th. of August 1812. Pub^d. by Ch^s. D. Veechio, 136 Broad Way. ☆ Designed and engraved by Thomas Gimbrede, being a second state of the foregoing print. Undated.

Stipple engraving. 6⅛ in. by 9⅜ in. Colored by hand. ☆ Fielding 513ii.

44

Plate 1st Preparing for an Engagement. The Constitution clearing for Action & bearing down La Guerrière Laying too. ☆ *Painted by Michael Cornée under Directions from Commodore Hull & Capt. Morris. Novr 1, 1812 Published according to Act of Congress & Engraved by J. R. Smith Boston.*

Aquatint. 7¹⁵⁄₁₆ in. by 12⅛ in. One of a set of three prints. ☆ Fielding 1456.

45

Plate 2^d Close Engagement. The Constitution in 15 Minutes fire carries away La Guerrièrs Mizen Mast. ☆ *Painted by Michael Cornée under Directions from Commodore Hull & Capt Morris.* ☆ *Nov^d 1st 1812 Published according to Act of Congress & Engraved by J. R. Smith Boston.*

Aquatint. 8¹⁄₁₆ in. by 12³⁄₁₆ in. Companion piece to the foregoing and to the following print. ☆ Fielding 1457.

46

Plate 3^d Surrender. The Constitution in 15 Minutes more fighting totaly dismasts La Guerrièr who fires her lee Gun. ☆ *Painted by Michael Cornée under Directions from Commodore Hull & Capt Morris.* ☆ *Novr 1st 1812 Published according to act of Congress & Engraved by J. R. Smith Boston.*

Aquatint. 8 in by 12⅛ in. Companion piece to the two foregoing prints. Fielding 1458.

The original paintings by M. Corné, after which these three aquatints were engraved, are now in the possession of the New Haven Colony Historical Society.

MICHELE CORNÉ was an Italian-born artist, whose reputation as a painter was established after he came to America. He painted a number of views of American naval engagements, some of which are reproduced in engravings and woodcuts contained in Abel Bowen's *The Naval Monument.*

JOHN RUBENS SMITH (circa 1770–1849) was born in England, a son of the famous English engraver, John Raphael Smith. The son first worked in Boston as an engraver. About 1816, he came to New York, where he painted portraits, engraved prints and conducted a drawing school. His pupils included Sully, Agate, Cummings, S. R. Gifford and Leutze. Subsequently, Smith did engraving and taught drawing in Philadelphia. He was a capable and experienced engraver.

47

Capture of The British Frigate Gurriere By The U. S. Frigate Constitution T. Birch A.C.S.A. D. Kimberly Sc. Undated.

Line engraving. 4$^{15}\!/_{16}$ in. by 7$^{7}\!/_{16}$ in. Colored by hand.

LENT BY ROBERT FRIDENBERG.

A similar engraving was published by Samuel Walker, Boston, as a book illustration.

DENISON KIMBERLY was born at Guilford, Conn., in 1814. He learned engraving in the establishment of Asaph Willard at Hartford. Kimberly had considerable success as a line engraver of portraits. In 1830, he was working in Boston for Samuel Walker, the Boston publisher. About 1858 Kimberly abandoned engraving for painting, chiefly doing portrait work. He had a studio in Hartford and in Manchester.

48

Constitution and Guerriere ☆ W. Charles Sc. ☆ Undated.

Line engraving. 4 in. by 7¼ in. In black and white.

LENT BY HENRY O. HAVEMEYER.

WILLIAM CHARLES came to New York from Scotland in 1801. Within a few years he had set himself up in that city as an engraver and publisher, later transferring his activities in this field to Philadelphia. Charles is best known for a series of caricatures mostly concerning events of the War of 1812, issued in 1813. Charles published *The Vicar of Wakefield* and *The Tour of Dr. Syntax*, both illustrated with colored plates aquatinted by him after designs by Rowlandson. He died in Philadelphia in 1820.

49

Prise de la frégate anglaise Guerrière, par la frégate américaine la Constitution. The English frigate Warrior Captur'd By the american frigate Constitution. ☆ *Dessiné par Montardier du Havre. Gravé par Baugean. Nº. 4.* ☆ *A Paris, chez Jean, rue Sᵗ. Jean de Beauvais, Nº. 10.* ☆ Undated.

Line engraving. 11³⁄₁₆ in. by 16⅞ in. In black and white. ☆ Published about 1814.

LENT BY ESTATE OF FRANCIS P. GARVAN.

In another state of this print, owned by Henry O. Havemeyer, the reference to Montardier has been omitted.

50

La Frégate Américaine La Constitution Prenant à l'abordage, La Frégate Anglaise La Guerriere Après 30 minutes de Combat, le 19 Aout 1812. Stradonwort Pinx. Valnest sculp. ☆ *A Paris chez Basset, Rue S. Jacques, Nº. 64. Déposé.* Undated.

Aquatint. 12⅞ in. by 13³⁄₁₆ in. Colored by hand. ☆ Published about 1815.

LENT BY ESTATE OF FRANCIS P. GARVAN.

51

Engagement between the American Frigate The Constitution, and the English Frigate The Guerriere, surrendered after having been entirely disabled. Combat entre la Frégate Americaine la Constution, et la Frégate Anglaise la Guerriere, qui s'est rendue aprés avoir été entierement désemparée. Dedicated to the Deffenders of the Seas. ☆ *Baugean del. Jazet sculp.* ☆ *Deposé A Paris chez Ostervald l'ainé Editeur, Rue de la Parcheminerie Nº. 2.* ☆ Undated.

Aquatint. 11⅜ in. by 16½ in. Colored by hand.

LENT BY ESTATE OF FRANCIS P. GARVAN.

52

Combat between the Frigate Constitution & the British Frigate Guerriere. ☆ *Publᵈ. by Risso 425 Pearl Sᵗ. N. York*

Line engraving. 8⅝ in. by 12¾ in. In black and white.

LENT BY HENRY O. HAVEMEYER.

53

The Constitution Bearing Down For The Guerriere. ☆ *M. Corne p. A. Bowen, sc.*
☆ Undated.

Woodcut. 3¼ in. by 6¹¹⁄₁₆ in. Colored by hand.

LENT BY ESTATE OF FRANCIS P. GARVAN.

A similar woodcut by Abel Bowen, inscribed "The Constitution Bearing Down
For The Guerriere," without the names of M. Corne and A. Bowen, is used as an
illustration in Bowen's *The Naval Monument*, published in 1816.

54

The Constitution In Close Action With The Guerriere. ☆ *M. Corne p. A. Bowen,
sc.* ☆ Undated.

Woodcut. 3⁵⁄₁₆ in. by 6¾ in. Colored by hand.

LENT BY ESTATE OF FRANCIS P. GARVAN.

A similar woodcut by Abel Bowen, inscribed "The Constitution In Close Action
With The Guerriere," without the names of M. Corne and A. Bowen, is used as an
illustration in Bowen's *The Naval Monument*, published in 1816.

55

Naval Heroes of the United States. No. 4. Constitution and Guerriere. Around view
of naval engagement in center are six oval portraits of American naval commanders.
☆ *Lith. & Pub. by N. Currier, 2 Spruce St. N.Y.* ☆ *Entered according to Act of
Congress in the year 1846 by N. Currier, in the Clerk's office of the District Court
of the Southern District of N.Y.*

Lithograph. 9¼ in. by 12¼ in. Colored by hand. ☆ H. T. Peters's Currier & Ives
1939.

56

*The Constitution And Guerriere. Fought, August 19. 1812. The Guerriere had 15
men killed & 63 wounded. The Constitution had 7 men killed & 7 wounded.* ☆ *Lith.
& Pub. by N. Currier, 2 Spruce Sᵗ. N.Y.* ☆ *Copyright 1846.*

Lithograph. 8³⁄₁₆ in. by 12½ in. Colored by hand. ☆ H. T. Peters's Currier & Ives
1123.

LENT BY HENRY O. HAVEMEYER.

La Constitution et La Guerriere + *The Constitution and The Guerriere* ☆ *Lith. par Betremieux. r. des Vinaigriers Nº. 25 Déposé. Chez Lordereau Rue Sᵗ. Jacques, Nº. 59 à Paris* ☆ Undated.

Lithograph. 18¾ in. by 25½ in. In black and white.

LENT BY HENRY O. HAVEMEYER.

Companion piece to lithograph by Betremieux of the engagement between the *United States* and *Macedonian*.

The Capture of The Guerriere By The Constitution, After an action of 55 minutes. American Loss; 7 killed, 7 wounded. British Loss; 15 killed, 62 wounded, 24 missing. ☆ *Lith. & Pub. By Sarony & Major, 99 Nassau near Fulton Sᵗ. N. Y.* ☆ *Entered according to act of Congress, A.D. 1848, by Sarony & Major in the Clerk's Office of the Dist. Court of Southern Dist. of N. York.*

Lithograph. 8⁵⁄₁₆ in. by 12¹⁵⁄₁₆ in. Colored by hand.

LENT BY THE FRANKLIN D. ROOSEVELT LIBRARY, HYDE PARK, N. Y.

The Constitution and Guerriere Fought August 19, 1812. The Guerriere had 15 men killed & 63 wounded. The Constitution had 7 men killed & 7 wounded. 427. ☆ *Lith. of E. C. Kellogg, 87 Fulton St. N. Y. & 73 Main St. Hartford, Ct. Horace Thayer & Cº. 127 Main St. Buffalo.* ☆ Undated.

Lithograph. 8⅛ in. by 12½ in. Colored by hand.

LENT BY ESTATE OF FRANCIS P. GARVAN.

WASP AND FROLIC
OCTOBER 18, 1812

The fortunes of war suddenly reversed this notable victory for the U. S. Navy, and deprived the *Wasp* of a well-earned capture, effected after a brilliant engagement with the *Frolic*.

On October 13, 1812, the American sloop-of-war *Wasp*, 18 guns, under the command of Master Commandant Jacob Jones, sailed from the Delaware on a cruise designed to prey on British shipping between South America, the

West Indies and England. After following five strange sail during the night of October 17th, Captain Jones found the next morning that this fleet consisted of six large British merchant ships under convoy of the British sloop-of-war *Frolic*, commanded by Captain Whinyates, a ship of practically the same fighting strength as the *Wasp*. The convoy was bound from Honduras to England.

Although the sea was high and the rigging of the *Wasp* had been damaged in a recent blow, Captain Jones put his ship in position for an engagement. The two vessels soon came within fifty or sixty yards of each other, and a furious battle at close range ensued. A contemporaneous account states: "The sea was so rough that the muzzles of the *Wasp's* guns were frequently in the water. The Americans, therefore, fired as the ship's side was going down, so that their shot went either on the enemy's deck or below it, while the English fired as the vessel rose and thus her balls chiefly touched the rigging or were thrown away."

The rigging of the *Wasp* became in such a precarious condition that Captain Jones brought his ship alongside for boarding. Several American seamen, with Lieutenant James Biddle, sprang on board the British ship. They found none alive on the deck of the *Frolic*, except the wheelsman and three officers, who threw down their swords in token of surrender. Lieut. Biddle climbed into the rigging of the *Frolic* and hauled down the British colors. Soon thereafter both masts of the *Frolic* fell. The severe action had lasted forty-three minutes after the first shot was fired by the *Frolic*. The losses on board the *Wasp* were six killed and five wounded.

While the *Wasp* and her prize sought to care for the wounded and to repair the havoc wrought by the action, the British ship-of-the-line, *Poictiers*, 74 guns, hove into sight and fired upon these ships. She was too formidable an opponent for the *Wasp* and the *Frolic* in their damaged condition, and both were compelled to surrender about two hours after their own fight had been concluded.

60

The Capture of H. B. M. Sloop of War Frolic, Cap^{n}*. Whinyates, by the U. S. Sloop of War Wasp, Cap*^{n}*. Ja*^{b}*. Jones, on the 18*th*. of Oct*^{r}*. 1812, after a close Action of 43 Minutes. Soon after the Frolic Surrendered, both her Masts went by the Board:*

She had 6 Merchant's Ships, under her Convoy. Statement of armament and losses of each ship is given at the sides. ☆ *Drawn & Engraved by F. Kearny, from a Sketch by Lieu^t. Claxton, of the Wasp.* ☆ *Pub^l. by C. P. Fessenden N°. 7 S. Seventh S^t. Philad^a.*

Aquatint. 11⅞ in. by 16⅞ in. Colored by hand. ☆ Second state. ☆ Stauffer 1581.

In his official report to the Secretary of the Navy, Capt. Jones stated: "Lieut. Claxton, who was confined by sickness, left his bed a little previous to the engagement; and though too indisposed to be at his division, remained upon deck, and showed by his composed manner of noting its incidents that we had lost by his illness the services of a brave officer." Presumably, Lieut. Claxton based his sketch upon the notes so made.

The first state of this print was published by F. Kearny. A third state was published by Prentiss and Whitney, Boston.

61

Capture of H. B. M. Sloop of War Frolic 22 Guns Capt. Whinyates By the U. S. Sloop of War Wasp 18 Guns, Capt. Jones. After an action of Fortyfive Minutes. ☆ *On board the Wasp 5 Killed. 5 wounded. On board the Frolic 30 Killed. 40 or 50 Wounded.* ☆ *J. J. Barralett, del. S. Seymour sculp.* ☆ *Philad. Publish'd by W. H. Morgan 114 Chestnut Street.*

Aquatint. 11⅞ in. by 16⅞ in. Colored by hand. ☆ Fielding 1429.

62

Capture of the British Sloop of War Frolic of 24 guns, by the U.S. Sloop of War Wasp of 18 guns. ☆ *Th. Birch Inv^t S. Seymour Sc.* ☆ *Copy right Secur'd*

Line engraving. 3⅜ in. by 5⅞ in. Colored by hand. ☆ Stauffer 2880.

63

Prise de la corvette anglais Forlic par la corvette americaine Wasp. The English sloop of war Forlic captur'd By the American sloop of war Wasp. ☆*Dessiné par Montardier du Havre. Gravé par Baugean.* ☆ *A Paris, chez Jean, Rue S^t. Jean de Beauvais N°. 10.* ☆ Undated.

Line engraving. 11⅛ in. by 16⅞ in. Colored by hand. ☆ Published about 1814.

UNITED STATES AND MACEDONIAN
OCTOBER 25, 1812

A few months after hostilities began in June 1812, the American naval authorities took advantage of England's preoccupation with the war in Europe and sent out squadrons or single ships to raid British commerce on the high seas.

On October 8, 1812, the frigates *President, Congress* and *United States* and the brig *Argus* departed from Boston on such a cruise. When clear of any enemy ships which might be lurking off the American coast, this fleet separated, the *United States* and the *Argus* under the command of Commodore Stephen Decatur heading in a direction south of the Canary Islands. Subsequently, the *Argus* was despatched to operate by herself.

Several hundred miles west of the Canary Islands, the *United States*, a frigate of 44 guns, carrying the flag of Commodore Decatur, encountered on October 25, 1812, the two-year old British frigate *Macedonian*, 38 guns, commanded by Captain John S. Carden. The British captain chose to relinquish his sailing superiority and to engage the more powerful American man-of-war.

Captain Decatur and most of his crew had been together on various ships for many years. The *United States* was maneuvered with great skill and used her long range guns to advantage before the battle reached close quarters. After ninety minutes of fighting, during a large part of which the *United States* maintained an incessant and effective broadside fire, the *Macedonian* had lost her mizzen-mast, fore and main topmasts and main yard and had suffered considerable injury to the hull. Her colors were then lowered in surrender.

This was a decisive victory. Five were killed and seven wounded on the *United States*, which was little damaged. On board the *Macedonian* there were thirty-six killed and sixty-eight wounded.

Commodore Decatur returned to the United States with his prize, in charge of Lieutenant William H. Allen, reaching Newport, R. I., early in December 1812. Great was the public enthusiasm over this signal naval achievement, following so closely after the capture of the *Guerrière* by the *Constitution*.

64

This Representation of the U. S. Frigate United States, Stephen Decatur Esqʳ. Commander, Capturing His Britannic Majesty's Frigate Macedonian, John S. Carden Esqʳ. Commander Is respectfully inscribed to Capt. Stephen Decatur his Officers and Gallant Crew by their devoted humble Servant James Webster. Fought Octʳ. 25″. 1812. ☆ Small bust portrait of Captain Decatur at center of bottom margin. ☆ *The Macedonian had 36 killed and 68 wounded. The United States had 5 killed and 7 wounded.* ☆ *Painted by T. Birch, A.S.C.A. Engraved by S. Seymour* ☆ *Philadᵃ Published May 1815 by James Webster.* ☆ *Subscription Price $5.00.*

Line engraving. 17⅞ in. by 26 in. In black and white. ☆ Stauffer 2879 ☆ Companion piece to the print of the action between the *Constitution* and the *Guerrière*, engraved by C. Tiebout after the painting by T. Birch.

LENT BY BEVERLEY R. ROBINSON.

65

Capture of H. B. M. Frigate Macedonian, Captⁿ. John S. Carden by the U. S. Frigate United States, Stephen Decatur Esqʳ. Commander. ☆ *To Commodore Decatur, his Officers and Brave Crew; This Plate is Dedicated with the greatest respect By B. Tanner & J. Webster.* ☆ Extracts from Commᵒ. Decatur's Official Letter follow. Statement of armament and losses of each ship at right side. ☆ *Painted by T. Birch, A. C. S. A. & P. A. Engraved by B. Tanner, A. C. S. A.* ☆ Vignette bust of Capt. Decatur at center of bottom margin, inscribed: *October 25, 1812. "Free Trade And No Impressment."* ☆ *Entered according to Act of Congress, the 13ᵗʰ. day of August 1813 by Benjamin Tanner of the State of Pennsylvania. Published 25ᵗʰ. October, 1813, by B. Tanner, Engraver, Nᵒ. 74 South Eighth Street, & J. Webster, Philadelphia.*

Line engraving. 19¹⁄₁₆ in. by 26 in. In black and white. ☆ First state.   *Illustrated*

LENT BY ROBERT FRIDENBERG.

65a

United States and Macedonian. ☆ *Extract from Commodore Decatur's Official letter: "At Sea, Octʳ. 30ᵗʰ. 1812. On the 25ᵗʰ. Insᵗ. being in latitude 29 degˢ. N. longitude 29 degˢ. 30 minˢ. W. we fell in with, and after an action of an hour and a half, captured his Britanic Majesty's Ship, Macedonian commanded, by Captain John Carden, and mounting 49 carriage Guns." The U. States had 5 Killed & 7 Wounded the Macedonian 36 K & 68 W.* ☆ *Painted by T. Birch. Engraved by*

CAPTURE of H.E.M. FRIGATE *MACEDONIAN* Captⁿ JOHN SURMARES by the U.S. FRIGATE *UNITED STATES*, STEPHEN DECATUR Esqr Commander.

ENGAGEMENT BETWEEN UNITED STATES AND MACEDONIAN, OCTOBER 25, 1812   (See No. 65)

Engraved by Benjamin Tanner after a painting by Thomas Birch

B. Tanner. ☆ *Published 1ˢᵗ. November 1814, by B. Tanner, Engraver, Nº. 74 South Eighth Street, Philadelphia. Entered according to Act of Congress the 13ᵗʰ day of August 1813 by Benjamin Tanner of the State of Pennsylvania.*

Line engraving. 16¹⁵⁄₁₆ in. by 24⅛ in. Colored by hand. ☆ Stauffer 3143. Parker 227–c.

LENT BY IRVING S. OLDS.

BENJAMIN TANNER published a set of three companion prints of American naval engagements, of which this is one. The others are: "Perry's Victory on Lake Erie, September the 10ᵗʰ. 1813," engraved by B. Tanner after the drawing by J. J. Barralet; and "Macdonough's Victory on Lake Champlain and Defeat of the British Army at Plattsburg by Genˡ. Macomb, Septʳ. 11ᵗʰ. 1814," engraved by B. Tanner after the painting by H. Reinagle.

66

Capture of H. B. M. Frigate Macedonian 38 Guns Capt. Carden By the Frigate United States 44 Guns Commodore Decatur. After a close action of Seventeen Minutes. On board the United States 5 Killed. 7 Wounded. On board the Macedonian 36 Killed. 68 Wounded. ☆ *J. J. Barralett del. S. Seymour sc.* ☆ *Philad. Publish'd by W. H. Morgan 114 Chestnut Street.*

Aquatint. 11¼ in. by 16⅞ in. Colored by hand. ☆ Fielding 1430.

LENT BY HENRY O. HAVEMEYER.

67

United States and Macedonian Frigates passing Hurl Gate for New York. Being the first British Frigate brought into the U. States during the Late War, fireing a salute as they pass'd. ☆ *Published by P. H. Hansell Carver and Gilder Nº 177 Race Sᵗ. Philadel.ᵃ. 1817.* ☆ *Artist and engraver not named.*

Line engraving. 11¾ in. by 18¹⁵⁄₁₆ in. Colored by hand. ☆ Hurl Gate was an old name for the entrance from Long Island Sound into the East River at New York, now known as Hell Gate. *Illustrated*

LENT BY HALL PARK McCULLOUGH.

68

The United States And The Macedonian. ☆ Artist, engraver and publisher not named. ☆ Undated.

Aquatint. 4⅞ in. by 7⁷⁄₁₆ in. Colored by hand.

LENT BY HENRY O. HAVEMEYER.

FRIGATE UNITED STATES AND HER PRIZE, THE MACEDONIAN,
PASSING HELL GATE FOR NEW YORK

Published by P. H. Hansell, Philadelphia

(See No. 67)

69

The United States And Macedonian. ☆ A. Bowen, del. et sc. ☆ Entered according to act of Congress.

Woodcut. 3¼ in. by 6¾ in. Colored by hand.

LENT BY ESTATE OF FRANCIS P. GARVAN.

A similar woodcut by Abel Bowen, without his name, inscribed "The United States And Macedonian," is used as an illustration in Bowen's *The Naval Monument,* published in 1816.

70

Prise de la frégate anglaise Macédonian, par la frégate américaine united States. The English frigate Macedonian Captur'd By the american United States. ☆ Dessiné par Montardier du Havre. Gravé par Baugean. N°. 3. ☆ Undated.

Line engraving. 11⅝ in. by 17¼ in. In black and white. ☆ Published about 1814. ☆ Parker 227–b.

LENT BY PEABODY MUSEUM, SALEM, MASS.

Another state of this print bears a publication line reading: *A Paris, chez Jean Rue S*ᵗ*. Jean de Beauvais N°. 10.*

71

Engagement between the American Frigate, the United States and the English Frigate the Macedonian surrendering after 17 minutes of fighting. Combat entre la Frégate Americaine les Etats Unis, et la Frégate Anglaise le Macedonian, qui s'est rendue après 17 minutes d'engagement. Dedicated to the Deffenders of the Seas. ☆ Baugean del. Jazet sculp. ☆ Déposé. A Paris chez Ostervald l'aîné Editeur, Rue de la Parcheminerie N°. 2 ☆ Undated.

Aquatint. 11⅛ in. by 16⁵⁄₁₆ in. Colored by hand. ☆ Parker 227–a.

LENT BY ESTATE OF FRANCIS P. GARVAN.

72

*Les Etats Unis et le Macedonian + The United States and Macedonian ☆ Chez Lordereau r. S*ᵗ*. Jacques N°. 59, à Paris Déposé ☆ Lith de Betremieux Fecit. ☆ Undated.*

Lithograph. 19 in. by 25½ in. In black and white.

LENT BY HENRY O. HAVEMEYER.

Companion piece to lithograph by Betremieux of the engagement between the *Constitution* and *Guerrière.*

73

The U. S. Frigate United States Capturing H. B. M. Frigate Macedonian. Fought, Octr. 25th. 1812. ☆ Lith. & Pub. by N. Currier, 2 Spruce S^t. & 169 Broadway, N. Y. ☆ Undated.

Lithograph. 7 15/16 in. by 12 7/8 in. Colored by hand. ☆ Harry T. Peters's Currier & Ives 1178.

LENT BY BEVERLEY R. ROBINSON.

74

The U. S. Frigate United States Capturing The British Frigate Macedonian. Fought, Octr. 25th. 1812 ☆ Lith. of E. C. Kellogg, 87 Fulton St. N. York & 73 Main St. Hartford, Conn. Horace Thayer & Co. 127 Main St. Buffalo 426. ☆ Undated.

Lithograph. 8 1/8 in. by 12 5/8 in. Colored by hand.

LENT BY ESTATE OF FRANCIS P. GARVAN.

75

The U. S. Frigate United States Capturing H. B. M. Frigate Macedonian. Fought, Octr. 25th. 1812. ☆ Kelloggs & Thayer, 144 Fulton St. N. Y. E. B. & E. C. Kellogg, 136 Main St. Hartford Conn. D. Needham, 233 Main St. Buffalo ☆ Undated.

Lithograph. 7 15/16 in. by 12 5/8 in. Colored by hand.

LENT BY ESTATE OF FRANCIS P. GARVAN.

76

Seetreffen Zwischen Dem Amerikanischen Schiffe "United States" Und Dem Brittischen Schiffe "Macedonian". Description of engagement in German, taken from report of Commodore Decatur, follows. ☆ *Auf Stein gez. v. Franz Kretzschmann. Lith. Inst. v. Rud. Weber, Leips. Gedr. v. W. Wörner.* ☆ Undated.

Lithograph. 16 3/8 in. by 22 1/4 in. In black and white.

LENT BY ESTATE OF FRANCIS P. GARVAN.

CONSTITUTION AND JAVA
DECEMBER 29, 1812

The year 1812 ended with another glorious American victory at sea — the fifth successful single-ship action in succession since the beginning of the war on June 18, 1812. The U. S. Navy gained a marked reputation and prestige by these demonstrations of seamanship and fighting skill against ships of the world's greatest naval power.

On October 26, 1812, the frigate *Constitution*, 44 guns, under the command of Commodore William Bainbridge set sail from Boston in company with the sloop-of-war *Hornet*, 18 guns, Captain James Lawrence. The two ships headed for the Cape Verde Islands, and from there to the South Atlantic. Their mission was to harass and destroy British shipping, it being the program of the Navy to utilize for this purpose all available units of the American fleet.

In December the *Constitution* sailed off alone in search of prizes, leaving the *Hornet* off Bahia, Brazil, to watch the *Bonne Citoyenne*, a British sloop-of-war in that port. On December 29, 1812, Captain Bainbridge came on the British frigate *Java*, 38 guns, Captain Henry Lambert, near the Brazilian coast, together with a captured American merchantship.

When the *Java* bore down, the *Constitution* opened fire at long range. An action lasting more than two hours followed, the latter part being at close quarters. Early in the action, Captain Bainbridge was twice wounded, but continued to direct the battle from on deck.

When the maneuverability of the *Java* was interfered with by the loss of her bowsprit and jib-boom and other injuries to the rigging, Captain Lambert put his ship into position for boarding. Before such an operation could be attempted, direct and accurate American gunfire caused the *Java's* foremast to go overboard, and soon thereafter her main topmast and mizzen-mast fell in succession, leaving the *Java* completely dismasted and practically helpless.

When the *Constitution*, after repairing injuries to her own rigging, came within closer range so as to rake the badly crippled British ship, if necessary, the *Java* struck her colors. Captain Lambert had been mortally wounded, and 21 others killed and 102 wounded. The *Constitution's* losses amounted to 9 killed and 25 wounded.

The *Java* was burned at sea by Captain Bainbridge, her damaged condition and the distance to North America not warranting an attempt to bring the frigate home as a prize. The *Constitution* returned to the United States, arriving at Boston on February 27, 1813.

77

Dedicated by Permission to The Right Honorable The Lords Commissioners of The Admiralty. ☆ *Plate 1. Situation of His Majesty's Frigate Java, Captain Lambert, at 5 Min. past 3 P.M. after an hours close & severe Action with the American Frigate Constitution, in which she was so much disabled in her Masts, Sails & Rigging, by the Enemy's very superior Force & Weight of Metal, that in the attempt to Board, with every prospect of success, her Foremast fell, & she was rendered totally unmanageable.* Statement of the number of men and armament of the English and American forces follows. ☆ *Drawn & Etch'd by N. Pocock, from a Sketch by Lieut. Buchanan.* ☆ *Engraved by R. & D. Havell.* ☆ *Jany. 1, 1814, Publish'd by Messrs. Boydell & Co. N°. 90 Cheapside, and Colnaghi & Co. Cockspur Street, London.*

Aquatint. 14 in. by 17^{15}⁄$_{16}$ in. Proof in black and white. One of a set of four prints.
Illustrated

78

Dedicated by Permission to The Right Honorable The Lords Commissioners of The Admiralty. ☆ *Plate 2nd. The Java, as she appeared at 35 Min. past 4 P. M. after having sustained several raking Broadsides from the Constitution whilst closely engageing her, untill she became a perfect Wreck, the Main Mast alone standing, the Rigging shot to pieces, and the Main Yard gone in the Slings. The Constitution making Sail & getting out of Gun Shot.* Statement of the number of armament and guns of the English and American forces follows. ☆ *Drawn & Etch'd by N. Pocock, from a Sketch by Lieut. Buchanan.* ☆ *Engraved by R. & D. Havell.* ☆ *Jany. 1, 1814, Publish'd by Messrs. Boydell & Co. N°. 90 Cheapside, and Colnaghi & Co. Cockspur Street, London.*

Aquatint. 14^1⁄$_{16}$ in. by 17^7⁄$_8$ in. Proof in black and white. The second of a set of four prints.

79

Dedicated by Permission to The Right Honourable The Lords Commissioners of The Admiralty. ☆ *Plate 3^d. The Java totally dismasted endeavouring to Wear by the assistance of a Jury Staysail hoisted to the Stump of the Foremast & Bowsprit; the Constitution Crossing her Bow in a Raking Position, Compels her to Surrender at 50 Min. past 5.* ☆ Statement of the number of men and armament of the English and American forces follows. ☆ *Drawn & Etch'd by N. Pocock, from*

ENGAGEMENT BETWEEN CONSTITUTION AND JAVA, DECEMBER 29, 1812

Plate 1 of four aquatints, engraved by R. & D. Havell from a drawing by Nicholas Pocock
after a sketch by Lieut. Buchanan   (See No. 77)

a Sketch by Lieut. Buchanan. ☆ Engraved by R. & D. Havell. ☆ Jany. 1, 1814,
Publish'd by Messrs. Boydell & Co. N°. 90 Cheapside, and Colnaghi & Co. Cock-
spur Street, London.

Aquatint. 14 in. by 18 in. Proof in black and white. The third of a set of four prints.

80

Dedicated by Permission to The Right Honourable The Lords Commissioners of
The Admiralty. ☆ Plate 4th. The Java in a Sinking state, set fire to, & Blowing
up. The Constitution at a distance ahead, Laying to, unbending Sails, repairing
her Rigging &c. on the Evening of 29th. Decr. 1812. ☆ Statement of the number
of men and armament of the English and American forces follows. *☆ Drawn &*
Etch'd by N. Pocock, from a Sketch by Lieut. Buchanan. ☆ Engraved by R. & D.
Havell. ☆ Jany. 1, 1814 Publish'd by Messrs. Boydell & Co. Cheapside, and Col-
naghi & Co. Cockspur Street, London.

Aquatint. 14 in. by 17⅞ in. Proof in black and white. The fourth of a set of four
prints. ☆ Parker 228–a.

ABOVE SET OF FOUR AQUATINTS LENT BY IRVING S. OLDS.

NICHOLAS POCOCK (1741–1821) was a nautically minded and talented British
marine painter. Before taking up painting as a profession, Pocock had been a ship-
master. He gained experience by making sketches at sea. Pocock produced numerous British marine paintings. His work was exhibited at the Royal Academy.
Engravings after his paintings of naval engagements appeared as illustrations in
The Naval Chronicle, first published in London in 1799 and continuing during the
early years of the nineteenth century. Pocock was also a print publisher in London.

R. & D. HAVELL was a prominent and highly skilled British engraving concern.
Robert Havell of this firm was the father of Robert Havell, Jr., who came to New
York about 1840 and remained in America the balance of his life. He is well known
as the engraver of most of the plates for Audubon's *Birds of America*. Robert
Havell, Jr. engraved a number of views of New York and other American cities.

81

To Commodore Bainbridge the officers Seamen & Marines of the United States
frigate Constitution this view of their Glorious capturing the British frigate the
Java off the coast of Brazils on the 29th X^{ber} 1812 after a Sanguinary conflict of 1
hour & 55 minutes, is with respect dedicated to them & the sons of freedom by
an admirer of American Valour & patriotism. ☆ Drawn under the direction of a

witness of the action by W. G. ☆ Artist not otherwise identified. Engraver and publisher not named. ☆ Undated.

Aquatint. 13 in. by 18⅜ in. Colored by hand.

82

The Capture of H. B. M. Frigate Java, Capt. Lambert, by the U. S. Frigate Constitution, Com. Bainbridge, on the 29th Decr. 1812. Lat. 13° 6′ S. Long. 38° W. off the coast of Brazil, after an engagement of 1 hour & 55 minutes. ☆ *Design'd & Engraved by N. Jocelin.* ☆ Undated.

Line engraving. 4¹⁵⁄₁₆ in. by 8⅝ in. Colored by hand. ☆ Fielding 744.

NATHANIEL JOCELYN (1796–1881) was born in New Haven, Conn. After being apprenticed to an engraver, he entered into partnership with Elkanah Tisdale, Mosley I. Danforth and Asaph Willard at Hartford, Conn., their engraving concern being known as the Hartford Graphic and Bank Note Engraving Company. With Danforth, he later founded the National Bank Note Engraving Company. About 1820, Jocelyn gave up engraving and became a meritorious and highly regarded portrait painter and eventually a member of the National Academy.

83

Le Combat Naval—Gloire Americaine. Prise glorieuse, du Vaisseau Anglais la Java, par la constitution, frégate Américaine, sur les côtes du Brésil, le 29 7ᵇʳᵉ. 1812; après un combat sanglant d'une heure 55 minutes. ☆ *Garneray del. Coqueret sc.* ☆ *A Paris chez M. Guerin vieille rue du Temple, Nᵒ. 75. Déposé.* ☆ Undated.

Aquatint. 12¹⁵⁄₁₆ in. by 18⅜ in. Colored by hand.

84

Prise de la frégate anglaise Java, par la frégate américaine la Constitution. The English Java, Captur'd By the american frigate Constitution. ☆ *Dessiné par Montardier du Havre. Gravé par Baugean.* ☆ *A Paris, chez Jean, rue Sᵗ. Jean de Beauvais, Nᵒ. 10.* ☆ Undated.

Line engraving. 10⅞ in. by 14⅝ in. Colored by hand. ☆ Published about 1814. ☆ Parker 228–b.

85

The Java Surrendering To The Constitution. ☆ *M. Corne, p. A. Bowen, sc.* ☆
Undated.

Woodcut. 3¼ in. by 6¾ in. Colored by hand.

LENT BY ESTATE OF FRANCIS P. GARVAN.

A similar woodcut by Abel Bowen, inscribed "The Java Surrendering To The
Constitution," without the names of Corne and Bowen, is used as an illustration in
Bowen's *The Naval Monument*, published in 1816.

86

*Constitution And Java. Fought Dec. 29th 1812. The Constitution had 9 killed and
25 wounded. The Java had 60 killed and 170 wounded.* ☆ *Lith. & Pub. by N. Currier, 2 Spruce St. N. Y. 403.* ☆ *Entered according to Act of Congress in the year
1846 by N. Currier, in the Clerk's office of the District Court of the Southern
District of N. Y.*

Lithograph. 7¾ in. by 12⅞ in. Colored by hand. ☆ H. T. Peters's Currier & Ives
1125.

LENT BY HENRY O. HAVEMEYER.

87

The capture of H. B. M^s. Sloop of War Java by the U. S. Frigate Constitution. ☆
Lith of D. W. Kellogg & Co. 110 Main St. Hartford Conn. ☆ Undated.

Lithograph. 8⁹⁄₁₆ in. by 12⅜ in. Colored by hand.

LENT BY ESTATE OF FRANCIS P. GARVAN.

88

*Diagram of the Action between the U. S. Frigate Constitution Com. Bainbridge and
H. M. Frigate Java Capt. Lambert.* ☆ *Two small views of the action inscribed:
Time—2 O'Clock & 50 min. P. M. and Time—5. O'Clock & 25 min. P. M.* ☆ *On
Stone by J. Queen.* ☆ *P. S. Duval, Lith. Phil^a.* ☆ *U. S. Military Magazine. Army &
Navy. Vol. 2nd.*

Lithograph. 10 in. by 7½ in. In black and white.

LENT BY HENRY O. HAVEMEYER.

HORNET AND PEACOCK

FEBRUARY 24, 1813

After a watch of eighteen days, the sloop-of-war *Hornet*, 18 guns, under the command of Captain James Lawrence, was compelled on January 24, 1813 to abandon its blockade of the British sloop-of-war *Bonne Citoyenne* in the harbor of Bahia, Brazil, because of the arrival of the 74-gun British ship *Montagu*. The *Hornet* evaded the *Montagu* by boldly slipping out of Bahia under the cover of darkness.

Captain Lawrence then leisurely started for home, raiding enemy commerce en route, in accordance with the instructions of Commodore William Bainbridge, whose ship, the *Constitution*, had originally accompanied the *Hornet* on this cruise. After capturing a valuable merchantman, Captain Lawrence on the afternoon of February 24, 1813, encountered the British brig *Peacock*, Captain William Peake, off Demerara, north of Surinam.

Captain Lawrence immediately ordered his men to quarters and had the *Hornet* cleared for action. The vessels soon came within range and exchanged broadsides at half pistol shot. The fire of the *Hornet* was so severe and damaging that within fifteen minutes the *Peacock* struck her colors and hoisted distress signals. Shortly thereafter her mainmast went by the board. The *Peacock* had been cut to pieces and was in a sinking condition. Despite a strenuous effort to save her, she sank before all of the prisoners could be removed, three of the rescuing crew from the *Hornet* being lost. In the action, one man was killed on the *Hornet* and four were wounded. The British losses were five killed, including Captain Peake, and thirty-three wounded.

The *Hornet* arrived safely at Holmes' Hole, Martha's Vineyard on March 19, 1813, completing a cruise of 145 days.

This was the first single-ship action of the war between English and American sloops-of-war.

89

The Hornet Blockading The Bonne Citoyenne ☆ *M. Corne, p. A. Bowen, sc.* ☆ Undated.

Woodcut. 3¼ in. by 6¹³⁄₁₆ in. In black and white.

LENT BY HENRY O. HAVEMEYER.

90

The Hornet Sinking The Peacock ☆ *M. Corne, p. A. Bowen, sc.* ☆ Undated.

Woodcut. 3¼ in. by 6¹³⁄₁₆ in. Colored by hand.

LENT BY DR. EUGENE H. POOL.

Two similar woodcuts, inscribed "The Hornet Blockading The Bonne Citoyenne" and "The Hornet Sinking The Peacock," without the names of Corne and Bowen, are used as illustrations in Bowen's *The Naval Monument*, published in 1816.

91

Hornet and Peacock (in pencil). ☆ *Hamlin aqᵗ.* ☆ Proof before letters. ☆ Undated.

Aquatint. 3½ in. by 5⁵⁄₁₆ in. In black and white. ☆ Stauffer 1246.

LENT BY HALL PARK McCULLOUGH.

92

The Hornet and Peacock, Or, John Bull in Distress. ☆ *Entered according to act of Congress the 27ᵗʰ of March 1813. by A. Doolittle of the State of Connecticut.* ☆ A line engraved caricature of a half-bull and half-peacock stung by an enormous hornet, which says: "Free Trade & Sailors Rights, you old rascal!"; the bull-peacock replying "Boo-o-o-o-hoo!!!"

6⁵⁄₁₆ in. by 10⁷⁄₁₆ in. Colored by hand. Stauffer 534.

LENT BY DR. EUGENE H. POOL.

AMOS DOOLITTLE (1754–1832) is one of the most famous of early American engravers, principally because he was among the first in this country to engrave historical plates. Born in Cheshire, Conn., his early training was as an apprentice to a silversmith, where he learned to engrave upon metals. After serving for a short time in the Continental Army, Doolittle engraved views of the battles at Lexington and Concord made by his friend, Ralph Earle. These engravings were published at New Haven in 1775. Doolittle's later work embraced portraits, historical scenes, book-plates, Bible illustrations and maps, done in line engraving. Doolittle designed and engraved at least three cartoons, two of them dealing with the War of 1812.

CAPTURE OF FORT GEORGE

MAY 27, 1813

Control of Lakes Ontario and Erie became a primary objective of the War of 1812, following the disastrous land campaign in the vicinity of Detroit at the outset of the war.

On August 31, 1812, the task of attaining this goal was entrusted to Captain Isaac Chauncey, who established his headquarters at Sackett's Harbor on the eastern end of Lake Ontario. Commodore Chauncey sought during the succeeding autumn and winter to build or acquire a sufficient fleet to assure American naval supremacy on these two lakes.

Toward the end of April 1813, Chauncey took on board his newly created Lake Ontario fleet a land force commanded by General Zebulon M. Pike and set sail from Sackett's Harbor. Aided by the guns of the fleet, the American troops landed near York (now Toronto) and gallantly took that British base, capturing a 14-gun schooner and a large quantity of naval and military stores. General Pike lost his life in this assault.

Commodore Chauncey soon undertook, with the aid of a land force under General Morgan Lewis, the capture of Fort George on the Canadian bank of the Niagara River opposite Fort Niagara. This British military post fell on May 27, 1813. The difficult responsibility of disembarking the soldiers for the attack on Fort George was in the hands of Colonel Winfield Scott and Master Commandant Oliver H. Perry, then temporarily detached from his post at Presqu'Isle (Erie).

The purpose of this campaign was to divert the enemy so as to enable Perry to complete, without undue interference, the fleet which he was then constructing at Erie, and to permit him to obtain a few vessels then lying in the Niagara River. These ends were achieved.

The absence of Commodore Chauncey's fleet at the western end of Lake Ontario, however, enabled the British at the other end of the lake to make a damaging raid upon the American base at Sackett's Harbor, thus aiding Sir James Yeo in his endeavor to prevent the American fleet from gaining naval supremacy on Lake Ontario.

93

Capture of Fort George. U. C. May 27th. 1813 by Major General Morgan Lewis & Commodore Chauncey. ☆ Drawn during the Battle by an Officer of Come. Chauncey's Flag Ship Madison. ☆ Engd. by Saml. Maverick, N. Y. ☆ Published & Sold by Samuel Maverick 35 Liberty St. New York.

Line engraving. 8⅜ in. by 13⅞ in. Colored by hand. ☆ Fielding 1068.

LENT BY WILLIAM H. COVERDALE COLLECTION.

94

Capture of Fort George. ☆ Artist and engraver not named. ☆ Undated. ☆ From *The Port Folio*, 1817.

Line engraving. 4½ in. by 7⅞ in. In black and white.

LENT BY ROBERT FRIDENBERG.

CHESAPEAKE AND SHANNON

JUNE 1, 1813

Three weeks prior to the engagement with the *Shannon*, Captain James Lawrence had been assigned to the command of the frigate *Chesapeake*, 36 guns, then being refitted at Boston. Before the *Chesapeake* was ready for her intended cruise at sea, the British frigate *Shannon*, 38 guns, a vessel of approximately equal size and strength, appeared in Massachusetts Bay. Her commander, Captain Philip B. V. Broke, sent a challenge to Captain Lawrence, which was not received.

Captain Lawrence was aware, however, of the presence of the *Shannon* off Boston and appeared eager to engage her. Immediately the refitting was completed, the *Chesapeake* sailed from Boston Harbor—about noon on June 1, 1813. The nearby *Shannon* was maneuvered so as to permit the *Chesapeake* to overtake her. When the vessels came within some 40 yards of each other, heavy broadsides were exchanged, considerably damaging the rigging of the *Chesapeake*. The contest continued fiercely yard-arm to yard-arm. Early in the action Captain Lawrence was wounded in the leg and shortly thereafter was carried below because of a more serious injury. He then uttered the famous message: "Don't give up the ship." Lieutenant Ludlow, the next in command, was also mortally wounded, as were nearly all of the other officers on the deck of the *Chesapeake*.

When the *Chesapeake* fouled the *Shannon*, Captain Broke led his boarders on to the American frigate, in order to crush the brave and determined resistance of his opponent. Within 15 minutes after the action commenced, most of the crew of the *Chesapeake* had been driven below deck and the American flag replaced by that of England.

[61]

The *Shannon* took her prize to Halifax, where Captain Lawrence died four days after the action. Later his body was buried in the churchyard of Trinity Church at New York.

The loss of the *Chesapeake* is an apt illustration of the importance of training, experience and preparedness in any test of military or naval strength. In the war with Tripoli and as commander of the *Hornet*, Captain Lawrence had proved himself a successful and courageous naval officer. Both he and Lieutenant Ludlow were new to the *Chesapeake*. His other officers were, for the most part, inexperienced. Recent replacements and untrained men comprised the majority of his crew, who had carried on no drills at sea. The battle was the first time the ship's company had ever been assembled at their stations. The *Shannon* was one of the crack frigates of the Royal Navy. Her commander, Captain Broke, and a large part of his crew had been together on this vessel for upwards of seven years.

95

This View of his Majesty's Ship Shannon, hove too, & cooly waiting the close approach of the American Frigate Chesapeak, who is bearing down to the Attack, with all the confidence of Victory; with its Companion the Capture of the Enemy; is with all due respect, & admiration of their intrepid conduct, most respectfully inscribed to Captain P. B. V. Broke and his gallant Ships Company, by their Obed. *Servant Rob*^t. *Dodd.* ☆ *Painted by R. Dodd from the information of Capt*ⁿ. *Falkinir.* ☆ *Published August. 1813, by R. Dodd, N*°. *3 Lucas Place, Commercial Road, and G. Andrews, N*°. *7, Charing Cross.*

One of a pair of aquatints. 13⅛ in. by 18⅜ in. Colored by hand.

96

To Captain P. B. V. Broke commanding his Majesty's Ship Shannon, his Officers, Seamen, & Marines, this representation of their gallantry boarding the American Frigate Chesapeak, being 110 Men superior in force and hauling down the Enemy's Colours in 15 Minutes from the commencement of the Action Is most respectfully Inscribed by their Ob^t. *Servant Rob*^t. *Dodd.* ☆ *Published August, 1813 by R. Dodd,*

N°. 3, Lucas Place, Commercial Road and G. Andrews, N°. 7, Charing Cross. ☆
After a painting by Robert Dodd.

The second of a pair of aquatints. 13¼ in. by 18⅜ in. Colored by hand.

ABOVE PAIR OF AQUATINTS LENT BY ESTATE OF FRANCIS P. GARVAN.

The original water color paintings by Robert Dodd, after which the above pair of aquatints were engraved, are in the Collection of Dr. Eugene H. Pool of New York.

97

To that distinguished Nobleman from whose Precepts & Example the British Navy has derived its present unrivalled state of Discipline and Glorious Preeminence John Earl of S^t. Vincent, K. B. late first Lord Commissioner of the Admiralty, Admiral of the Red, Lieu^t. General of Marines, &c—This View of the Commencement of the Action between His Majesty's Ship Shannon and the United States Frigate Chesapeake, off Boston Light House, on the 1st. of June, 1813, is respectfully Dedicated by his Lordship's obedient Servt. G. Webster. Statement of the armament, size of crew and losses of each ship follows. ☆ *Painted by John Theophilus Lee Esqr. Joseph Jeakes sculp^t.* ☆ *London, Published by G. Webster & C°. 21, White Lion Street, Pentonville, & Sold by R. Lambe, Printseller, 96, Gracechurch Street.* ☆ Undated.

One of a pair of aquatints. 15¾ in. by 22 in. Colored by hand. ☆ Second state, with the word "Preeminance" in the title corrected to "Preeminence."

98

To Captain Broke, the Officers, Seamen and Marines of His Majesty's Ship Shannon. This View of their Boarding & Capturing the American United States Frigate The Chesapeake, off Boston, on the 1st. of June, 1813, after a sanguinary Conflict of only fifteen minutes is with respect Dedicated to them, and the Admirers of British Valor, by their obedient Servant G. Webster. Statement of the armament, size of crew and losses of each ship follows. ☆ *Painted by G. Webster under the direction of Captⁿ. Falkner, late Lieut^t. of the Shannon during the Action. Jeakes sculp^t.* ☆ *Published by G. Webster, 21, White Lion Street, Penton Ville.* ☆ Undated.

The second of a pair of aquatints. 15½ in. by 21⅞ in. Colored by hand. ☆ Parker 231–b.

ABOVE PAIR OF AQUATINTS LENT BY ESTATE OF FRANCIS P. GARVAN.

A second state of this print was published in London in 1815 by J. Burr and G. Ballisat, Gracechurch St^r.

The Brilliant Achievement of the Shannon Frigate, Captⁿ. Broke in boarding and capturing the United States Frigate, Chesapeake off Boston, June 1st. 1813 in Fifteen Minutes. Shannon 38 Guns, 330 Men Chesapeake 49 Guns, 440 Men. ☆ Painted & Engraved by W. Elmes. ☆ Augt 1813 Pub^d by Wm Elmes—107 Tottenham Court Road London.

Aquatint. 14¼ in. by 19¼ in. Colored by hand.   *Illustrated*

LENT BY BEVERLEY R. ROBINSON.

IOO

To the Right Honorable Lord Viscount Melville first Lord of the Admiralty. This print of His Majesty's Frigate the Shannon, Captⁿ. Broke, Commander, carrying the American Frigate, Chesapeake, (commanded by Capt. Lawrence) by boarding in sight of Boston Harbour is respectfully inscribed by his Most obedient and devoted Humble Servant J. Hassell. Statement of number of guns and size of crew of each ship follows. ☆ *Painted by Thos. Whitcombe Aqua^a. Jeakes. ☆ London—Pub. Sept. 1—1813 by Hassell & Co. 11, Clements Inn.*

Aquatint. 15⅛ in. by 21¼ in. Colored by hand. ☆ First state.

LENT BY HENRY O. HAVEMEYER.

In the second state of this print, the inscription is by "His Lordship's Most obedient and devoted Humble Servants J. Hassell & Co." In the third state, the publication line was changed to read: "May 1st 1814 by Hassell and Richards, 344 Strand." In the fourth state, the publication line was altered to read: "London Pub^d. By W. Deeley, 6 Pleasant Place, Pentenville. 1838."

IOI

Plate 1.—To Captain Sir Philip Bowes Vere Broke, Bar^t. and K.C.B. This representation of H.M.S. Shannon, commencing the Battle with the American Frigate Chesapeake on the 1st. June 1813, is Dedicated by his obliged and most grateful Servant, R. H. King. ☆ Painted by J. C. Schetky Esqre. & on Stone by L. Haghe. ☆ Designed by Captⁿ. R. H. King, R.N. ☆ London, pub^d. by Smith Elder & Co. 65 Cornhill. ☆ Undated.

One of a set of four lithographs. 12 in. by 16⅞ in. Colored by hand.

ENGAGEMENT BETWEEN CHESAPEAKE AND SHANNON, JUNE 1, 1813

Painted, engraved and published by William Elmes

(See No. 99)

102

Plate 2.—To Captain Sir Philip Bowes Vere Broke, Bar^t. and K.C.B. This representation of the American Frigate Chesapeake, Crippled and thrown into utter disorder by the two first broadsides fired from H.M.S. Shannon, is Dedicated by his obliged and most grateful Servant, R. H. King. ☆ Painted by J. C. Schetky Esqre. & on Stone by L. Haghe. ☆ Designed by Capt. R. H. King R. N. ☆ London Pub^d. by Smith, Elder & Co. 65 Cornhill. ☆ Undated.

One of a set of four lithographs. 12¼ in. by 16¾ in. Colored by hand.

103

Plate 3.—To Captain Sir Philip Bowes vere Broke, Bar^t. and K.C.B. This representation of H.M.S. Shannon, carrying by boarding the American Frigate Chesapeake, after a cannonade of five minutes, on the 1st. June, 1813. is Dedicated by his obliged and most grateful Servant, R. H. King. ☆ Painted by J. C. Schetky Esqre. & on Stone by L. Haghe. Designed by Capt. R. H. King, R. N. ☆ London, pub^d. by Smith Elder & Co. 65 Cornhill. Print^d. by W. Day 17, Gate S^t. ☆ Undated.

One of a set of four lithographs. 12¼ in. by 16¾ in. Colored by hand.

104

Plate 4.—To Captain Sir Philip Bowes Vere Broke, Bar^t. and K.C.B. This representation of H.M.S. Shannon leading her Prize the American Frigate Chesapeake into Halifax Harbour, on the 6th. of June, 1813. is Dedicated by his obliged and most grateful Servant, R. H. King. ☆ Painted by J. C. Schetky Esqre. & On Stone by L. Haghe. Designed by Capt. R. H. King, R. N. ☆ London Pub^d. by Smith, Elder & Co. 65, Cornhill.

One of a set of four lithographs. 12¼ in. by 16¾ in. Colored by hand. ☆ Parker 231–a.

ABOVE SET OF FOUR LITHOGRAPHS LENT BY IRVING S. OLDS.

The original water color paintings from which these four lithographs were made are in the possession of Captain Saumarez, Broke Hall, Nacton, England.

105

Capture of the Chesapeake, June 1st 1813. ☆ Painted by T. Whitcombe Engraved by Bailey ☆ Published Jany. 1–1817 at 48 Strand, for J. Jenkins' Naval Achievements. Aquatint. 6¾ in. by 10⅛ in. Colored by hand. ☆ Parker 231–c.

LENT BY IRVING S. OLDS.

106

The Shannon Frigate, Capt. Broke, boarding & Capturing the American Frigate, Chesapeake, off Boston. June 1st. 1813 in Fifteen Minutes. ☆ *Painted by W. B. Walker, 4, Fox & Knot Court, Cow Lane, London.* ☆ Undated.

Mezzotint. 9 in. by 13¾ in. Colored by hand.

LENT BY IRVING S. OLDS.

107

Capture of The Chesapeake, June 1st. 1813. ☆ *Painted by T. Whitcombe. Engraved by W. J. Bennett. Executed under the direction of Captn. Sir P. B. V. Broke, Bar^t.* ☆ Undated.

Aquatint. 5⅛ in. by 8⅛ in. Colored by hand. ☆ Parker 231–d. ☆ From *The Naval Chronology of Great Britain*, Vol. III. by J. Ralfe.

LENT BY DR. EUGENE H. POOL.

108

Boarding and Taking the American Ship Chesapeake, by the Officers & Crew of H. M. Ship Shannon, Commanded by Capt. Broke, June 1813. ☆ *Heath del^t. M. Dubourg sculp^t.* ☆ *Published & Sold July 1, 1816, by Edwd. Orme, Publisher to His Majesty, & the Prince Regent, Bond Street, corner of Brook Street, London.* ☆ Published for *Orme's Historic Military and Naval Anecdotes*.

Aquatint. 7¾ in. by 11 in. Colored by hand. ☆ Parker 231–f.

LENT BY ESTATE OF FRANCIS P. GARVAN.

109

The Tars of Old England Triumphant A View of the Gallant Action Between His Majesty's Frigate The Shannon and The Chesapeake American Frigate. Was fought June 1, 1813 off Boston in America when after exchanging between two and three broadsides our brave Tars, boarded her and in two Minutes time the enemy were driven sword in hand from evrey post the American Flag was hawled down, and the proud old British Union floated trimphant over it, the Shannon was commanded by Capt. Broke, and had 23 Men slain and 56 Wounded, the Chesapeake Capt. Lawrence, had, himself and about 70 Killed, and 100 wounded. Table below of the principal incidents of the engagement, followed by a statement of the armament and size of crew of each ship. ☆ Artist and engraver not named. ☆ *Published July 24 1813 by G. Thompson Nᵒ. 43 Long Lane West, Smithfield.*

Line engraving. 13¼ in by 17¾ in. Colored by hand.

LENT BY HENRY O. HAVEMEYER.

110

The Chesapeake & Shannon. ☆ *M. Corné p. Wightman sc.* ☆ *Engraved for The Naval Monument.*

Line engraving. 3⁷⁄₁₆ in. by 6¹¹⁄₁₆ in. In black and white. ☆ Undated.

LENT BY HENRY O. HAVEMEYER.

111

Struck with the Gallantry, Skill, and Decision, Displayed by Sir. Philip Bowes Vere Broke, Baronet, K.C.B., Commander of his Majesty's Frigate, the Shannon, in the attack, boarding and capture of the American Frigate, the Chesapeake, of superior force in Men and Metal, and under the command of a distinguished Captain, off Boston Light House, on the first of June 1813, achieved in the short space of fifteen minutes: The Inhabitants of Suffolk, the Victor's Native Country, anxious to evince their sense of his spirited, judicious, and determined conduct in thus adding another brilliant Trophy to the unrivalled Triumphs of the British Navy, with a spontaneous burst of feeling, voted him this Tribute of their Affection, Gratitude and Admiration. ☆ *Manufactured by S. Hougham & Co. Henry Meyer Execudit.* ☆ *London Published for the Proprietor, Decʳ. 2ᵈ. 1816.*

Aquatint of a silver plateau presented to Captain Broke by the inhabitants of Suffolk. 15⅜ in. by 15¼ in. View of the engagement in the center is colored by hand. ☆ Parker 231–g.

LENT BY IRVING S. OLDS.

112

Boarding the Chesapeake. ☆ Artist and engraver not named. ☆ Undated.

Small circular aquatint. 2⅜ in. diameter. Colored by hand. ☆ From *The Naval and Military Exploits which Have Distinguished the Reign of George III*, by Jehoshaphat Aspin. Published by Samuel Leigh, 18, Strand, London, 1820.

LENT BY DR. EUGENE H. POOL.

113

The Boarding of The Chesapeake By the Crew of The Shannon. Death of Captain Lawrence. ☆ Published by the London Printing and Publishing Company, Ltd. ☆ Artist and engraver not named. ☆ Undated.

Line engraving. 4¾ in. by 7¼ in. Colored by hand.

LENT BY IRVING S. OLDS.

114

British Valour and Yankee Boasting or, Shannon versus Chesapeake. G. Cruikshank *fect* ☆ *Pub^d. September 1st 1813 for the Proprietor of Town Talk*

An engraved caricature. 7³⁄₁₆ in. by 19¹⁄₁₆ in. Colored by hand.

LENT BY ROBERT FRIDENBERG.

ARGUS AND PELICAN
AUGUST 14, 1813

On June 18, 1813 the brig *Argus*, 16 guns, Captain William Henry Allen, sailed from New York for the immediate purpose of taking to France our new Minister to that country, William H. Crawford. After landing her passenger at L'Orient, the *Argus* proceeded upon a cruise to raid enemy commerce in the vicinity of the British Isles. In the short space of a month, Captain Allen captured twenty vessels in the English and Irish Channels of a total estimated value of two million dollars.

Off Ireland, on the early morning of August 14, 1813, the *Argus* came on the British brig *Pelican*, 18 guns, Captain J. F. Maples. Captain Allen at once prepared to receive his adversary, and at 6 P.M. the action commenced within musket range. Almost immediately the American commander was shot in the leg and severely wounded. Shortly thereafter he fainted from loss of blood and had to be taken below. Within twenty-five minutes, the fire of the *Pelican* had so damaged the rigging and wheel ropes of the *Argus* as to make her unmanageable. This prevented the *Argus* from getting into a position to board the *Pelican*, which continued to rake her opponent.

The remainder of the fight is best described in the below quoted official report of Lieutenant W. H. Watson, who though wounded in the head and taken from the deck soon returned and assumed command: "From this time (when the crew of the *Argus* prepared to board) until 47 minutes after 6, we were opposed to a cross or raking fire, without being able to oppose but little more than musketry to the broadside of the enemy, our guns being much disabled and seldom brought to bear. The *Argus* having now suffered much, in hull and rigging, as also in killed and wounded . . .; and being exposed to a galling fire, which from the enemy's ability to manage his vessel, we could not avoid, I deemed it necessary to surrender, and was taken possession of by his Britannic majesty's sloop the *Pelican*. . . ."

Captain Allen died as a consequence of the wound received in the engagement and was buried at Plymouth, England, on August 21, 1813.

115

The Pelican Sloop of War, Capt. Maples, Rakeing & Capturing the American brig Argus, on the 14 of Augt. 1813, after an Action of 40 Minutes, the American Capt. Allen was Mortally Wounded. A statement of the armament and losses of each ship is given below the view. *Published by W. B. Walker, 4 Fox & Knot Court, Cow Lane, London.* ☆ Artist and engraver not named. ☆ Undated.

Mezzotint. 8⅞ in. by 13⅝ in. Colored by hand.

LENT BY IRVING S. OLDS.

116

Capture of the Argus, Augt. 14th. 1813 ☆ *Painted by T. Whitcombe. Engraved by T. Sutherland.* ☆ *Published Feby. 1 1817, at 48, Strand, for J. Jenkins' Naval Achievements*

Aquatint. 6¾ in. by 10¼ in. Colored by hand. ☆ Parker 232–a.

LENT BY IRVING S. OLDS.

117

Capture of the Argus, August 14th. 1813. ☆ *Painted by Whitcombe. Engraved by T. Sutherland.* ☆ *Published by Whitmore & Fenn, Charing Cross, Septr. 1, 1818.* ☆ Published for Ralfe's *Naval Chronology.*

Aquatint. 5¼ in. by 8³⁄₁₆ in. Colored by hand. ☆ Parker 232–b.

LENT BY HARRY S. NEWMAN.

ENTERPRIZE AND BOXER
SEPTEMBER 5, 1813

On September 1, 1813, the United States brig *Enterprize*, 14 guns, sailed from Portsmouth, N. H., under the command of Lieutenant William Burrows. Four days later, while in search of reported privateers, the *Enterprize* discovered the British brig *Boxer*, 14 guns, Captain Samuel Blythe, getting under way off the Maine coast.

Lieutenant Burrows gave chase and by mid-afternoon had maneuvered his ship into position for close action. Both vessels commenced firing when within half pistol shot. After forty minutes of continued fire at close range, during which the *Enterprize* was able twice to rake her opponent, the officers of the British brig hailed and said they had surrendered, "their colours being nailed to the masts, could not be hauled down."

Both Lieutenant Burrows and Captain Blythe received mortal wounds early in the engagement. The senior officer, Lieutenant Edward R. M'Call, assumed command of the *Enterprize* and concluded a brilliantly fought action. Lieutenant Burrows refused to be carried below until the *Boxer* had surrendered. He died shortly thereafter.

118

The Enterprise And Boxer. ☆ *M. Corne, p. A. Bowen, sc.* ☆ Undated.

Woodcut. 3¼ in. by 6¾ in. Colored by hand.

LENT BY ESTATE OF FRANCIS P. GARVAN.

A similar woodcut, without the names of Corne and Bowen, is used as an illustration in Bowen's *The Naval Monument,* published in 1816.

BATTLE OF LAKE ERIE
SEPTEMBER 10, 1813

Soon after Captain Isaac Chauncey was ordered to the command on Lakes Ontario and Erie on August 31, 1812, and directed to push the building or assembly of a naval force on each lake, a new base was established at Presqu'-

Isle (Erie). Control of Lake Erie was considered to be a vital military necessity.

Work was commenced in October 1812 upon the construction of two new brigs at Erie. Master Commandant Oliver H. Perry assumed command of this station in March 1813 and rushed the completion of these two brigs, as well as the building of two additional sloops-of-war. Ship carpenters to construct these vessels had to be brought from New York and other eastern points. Philadelphia was the main source of supply for the sails, cables and anchors required for the new fleet. Armament and naval stores were obtained principally from Pittsburgh and Buffalo. The powder was hauled through the woods from Wilmington, Delaware. Crews were assembled from such men as were available at Erie, Buffalo, and the posts on Lake Ontario and Lake Erie, many of whom had had little or no previous experience on board a man-of-war.

Following the capture of Fort George on May 27, 1813, Perry brought five small vessels from the Niagara River, and this much needed addition to his fleet safely reached Erie on June 19, 1813. By the first week in August, Perry's fleet was ready. On August 12, 1813, following the arrival at Erie of Lieutenant Jesse D. Elliott and ninety men, the fleet left Erie to meet the enemy, commanded by Commodore Robert H. Barclay.

Captain Perry established his fleet at Put-in-Bay (near Sandusky) so as to be in a position to watch Commodore Barclay's movements from his base at Malden across the lake, and also so as to be able to threaten the British line of communications westward from the middle of Lake Erie.

Early on the morning of September 10, 1813, Commodore Barclay's fleet was sighted. At once Perry sailed out with his nine vessels to engage the British fleet in accordance with a previously arranged plan of battle. The longer range of the British guns made an engagement at close range necessary. The battle flag of Perry "Don't Give Up the Ship" used the gallant words of the dying Captain Lawrence of the *Chesapeake*, after whom Perry's flagship was named.

At the beginning of the action, the three heaviest British ships centered their fire on the *Lawrence*, the leading ship in the American line of battle, and in about two hours reduced Perry's flagship to a disabled wreck. Perry then took to a small open boat and rowed to the undamaged *Niagara*, a sister ship of the *Lawrence,* of which he took command. Under Perry's direction, the signal for close action was given and the *Niagara* passed through the British line firing broadsides right and left. She was aided in this assault by some of Perry's smaller vessels under the command of Lieutenant Elliott. The fire of the *Niagara* and these other ships was so accurate and deadly that one by one the units of the British fleet surrendered. Commodore Perry returned to the damaged *Lawrence* to receive the swords of the surrendering British officers.

At the end of an action of more than three hours' duration, Commodore Perry was able to send his historic message to General William Henry Harrison: "We have met the Enemy and they are ours: two ships, two brigs, one schooner, and one sloop."

The British military position around Lake Erie collapsed as a consequence of this signal naval victory. Soon after Commodore Perry transported an American army under General Harrison across Lake Erie, which decisively defeated the British at the Battle of the Thames in Canada on October 5, 1813. Commodore Perry led a cavalry charge in this battle. Lake Erie was at last under complete American control.

119

Perry's Victory On Lake Erie. ☆ *Painted by T. Birch. Engraved by A. Lawson. Printed by B. Rogers.* ☆ *Published by Joseph Delaplaine.* ☆ *Undated.*

Line engraving. 18⅝ in. by 25⅝ in. In black and white. ☆ First state. ☆ Stauffer 1691. *Illustrated*

LENT BY ESTATE OF FRANCIS P. GARVAN.

A second state of this engraving bears a publication line reading: "Published by H. Quig N. E. cor 7th & Sansom St. Printed by C. Quig." Stauffer 1691ii.

A third state of this engraving bears a publication line reading: "Pub. by Wm. Smith, Print Seller, 702 South 3rd. St. Phil^a."

120

Perry's Victory on Lake Erie, September the 10th. 1813. Represents the position of the two Fleets, at the moment when the Niagara is pushing through the enemy's line, pouring her thunder upon them from both broadsides, and forcing them to

PERRY'S VICTORY ON LAKE ERIE.

BATTLE OF LAKE ERIE, SEPTEMBER 10, 1813

Engraved by Alexander Lawson after a painting by Thomas Birch

(See No. 119)

surrender in succession to the American Flag. Commodore Perry having a short time before left the Lawrence in a small boat, amidst a tremendous fire from the British Squadron, and hoisted his Flag on board the Niagara. The Lawrence is seen at a distance disabled. ☆ *Drawn by J. J. Barralet. Engraved by B. Tanner. Printed by Cammeyer & Acock.* ☆ *Published 1ˢᵗ. January 1815, by B. Tanner, Engraver, N°. 74 South Eighth Street, Philadelphia.* ☆ *Entered according to Act of Congress the 14ᵗʰ day of October 1814 by Benjamin Tanner of the State of Pennsylvania.*

Line engraving. 17¼ in. by 14¾ in. Colored by hand. ☆ Stauffer 3188ii.

LENT BY IRVING S. OLDS.

Companion piece to Benjamin Tanner's engravings of "United States and Macedonian" and "Macdonough's Victory on Lake Champlain, and Defeat of the British army at Plattsburg Genˡ. Macomb, Septʳ. 11ᵗʰ. 1814."

This engraving was published with a key, also included in this exhibition, entitled "Key to B. Tanner's Print of Perry's Victory."

There is an earlier state of this engraving without the line giving date of entry. Stauffer 3138i.

121

This representation of the Battle on Lake Erie, is respectfully inscribed to Commodore Perry, his Officers and gallant Crews; By their humble Servant, James Webster. Fought Sept. 10, 1813. ☆ *Drawn by Sully and Kearny. Engrᵈ. by Murray, Draper, Fairman and Co.* ☆ *Philadᵃ. Published 26 July 1815 by Murray Draper Fairman & Co. and J. Webster.* ☆ *Entered according to Act of Congress the 26 July 1815 by Murray Draper Fairman & Co. and J. Webster of the State of Pennsylvania.*

One of a pair of line engravings. 17¾ in. by 25¾ in. In black and white. ☆ First state. ☆ Stauffer 2288.

122

This representation of the Battle of Lake Erie is respectfully inscribed to Commodore Perry his Officers and gallant Crews By their humble Servant, James Webster. Fought Sepˡ. 10. 1813. Second View. ☆ *Drawn by Sully and Kearny Etched by C. Tiebout & Engraved by G. Murray. Printed by Rogers and Esler.* ☆ *Philadᵃ. Published 26 July 1815 by Murray Draper Fairman & Co. and J. Webster. Entered according to Act of Congress the 26 july 1815 by Murray Draper Fairman & Co. and J. Webster of the State of Pennsylvania.*

[75]

The second of a pair of line engravings. 18 in. by 25⅞ in. In black and white. ☆ First state. ☆ Stauffer 2289.

A later state of these engravings bears a publication line reading: "Published by Wm. Smith, Print Seller 702 So. 3rd St. Philad\.", without any date of publication. Stauffer 2288ii, 2289ii.

GEORGE MURRAY was born in Scotland. Before coming to Philadelphia about 1800, Murray had done portrait engraving in London. He became prominent in the Philadelphia Society of Artists. In 1810, Murray founded the bank-note and general engraving firm of Murray, Draper, Fairman & Co., which carried on an extensive and profitable business in Philadelphia for a number of years. Murray died in Philadelphia in 1822.

123

Brilliant Victory!! obtained by Commodore O. H. Perry over the British Fleet on Lake Erie, Commanded by Capt. Barclay. Septr 10th. 1813. A statement follows naming the vessels in the two fleets and the number of guns on each vessel. ☆ Artist, engraver and publisher not named. ☆ Undated.

Line engraving. 10⅜ in. by 16¼ in. Colored by hand.

This print has been attributed to Ralph Rawdon. No substantial evidence has been found, however, to substantiate such an attribution.

124

American Naval Victories. (at top) *Dont give up the Ship—Lawrence* (at bottom) *Glorious & Brilliant Victory Obtained By Commodore O. H. Perry Over The British Fleet On Lake Erie Commanded By Capt. Barclay. September 10th. 1813.* ☆ Oval view at top. Four small rectangular views at each side, inscribed *U. S. Frigate Constitution Capt. Hull Capturing H.B.M. Frigate Guerrier Capt. Dacres August 19th. 1812. Constitution Setting Fire To The Guerrier August 19th. 1812. U.S. Frigate U. States Commodore Decatur Capturing H.B.M. Frigate Macedonian Capt. Carden October 25th. 1812. U. S. Frigate Constitution Capt. Bainbridge Capturing H.B.M. Frigate Java Capt. Lambert December 29th. 1812. U.S. Sloop of War Wasp Captain Jones Capturing H.B.M. Sloop of War Frolic Capt. Whinyates October 18th. 1812. U.S. Sloop of War Hornet Capt. Lawrence Capturing H.B.M. Sloop of War Peacock Capt. Peak February 24th. 1813. U.S. Brig Enterprize Lieut. Comt. Burrows Capturing H.B.M. Boxer Captain Blyth Esqr. September 4th. 1813* (separate views of these two ships). ☆ American school sheet, containing now illegible handwritten poem in the center of the engraved surrounding borders. ☆ *N. York Published by J. Tiebout Nᵒ. 232 Water Sᵗ. December 1813.* ☆ *Printed by Riley & Adams 23 Chatham St. Copy Right Secured According to Law.*

Line engraving. 16¼ in. by 13½ in. Colored by hand. ☆ Fielding 1851.

LENT BY H. WUNDERLICH AND O. M. TORRINGTON.

125

Battle of Erie. ☆ *Printed by Samˡ. Maverick, New York.* ☆ *Engraved by P. Maverick. Newark, N. J.* ☆ Undated.

One of a pair of line engravings. 3¹⁵⁄₁₆ in. by 7¾ in. Colored by hand. ☆ Stauffer 2234.

126

Battle of Erie, 2ᵈ. View. ☆ *P. Maverick sc. Newark, N. J.* ☆ *Printed by Samˡ. Maverick, New York.* ☆ Undated.

The second of a pair of line engravings. 3⅞ in. by 7¾ in. Colored by hand. ☆ Stauffer 2235.

ABOVE PAIR OF ENGRAVINGS LENT BY ESTATE OF FRANCIS P. GARVAN.

PETER MAVERICK (1780–1831) was born in New York, a son of the early New York engraver, Peter Rushton Maverick. By 1802, Peter Maverick was in the engraving business in New York. Later he moved to Newark, New Jersey, where he formed a partnership with Asher B. Durand. Maverick soon returned to his native city and there conducted an extensive establishment as a general engraver and copperplate printer, finally adding lithography to his business. Peter Maverick was one of the founders in 1826 of the National Academy of Design. Samuel Maverick and Andrew Maverick were his brothers.

127

Commodore Perry's Victory, on Lake Erie, over the British fleet, commanded by Commodore Barclay, Sept. 10ᵗʰ. 1813 ☆ Artist and engraver not named. Print undoubtedly engraved by Abner Reed. ☆ *Published by A. Reed & Co. E. Windsor, Con. April 1814*

Line engraving. 6¾ in. by 10¼ in. Colored by hand.

LENT BY IRVING S. OLDS.

ABNER REED (1771–1866) first engaged in the engraving business at Hartford, Connecticut. In 1811, he returned to his place of birth, E. Windsor, Conn., becoming a well-known bank-note engraver. He formed a partnership with Samuel Stiles in 1821, the firm of Reed & Stiles continuing as engravers in Hartford until 1824. Later Reed worked as an engraver in New York, publishing in that city *Reed's Guide To the Art of Penmanship*, containing a number of his engraved plates.

128

Perry's Victory. ☆ Artist, engraver and publisher not named. ☆ Undated.

Aquatint. 12½ in. by 16¾ in. Colored by hand.

LENT BY IRVING S. OLDS.

129

First View of Com. Perry's Victory ☆ *M. Corne p. W. B. Annin Sc.* ☆ *Engraved for The Naval Monument.* ☆ *Copy right 1815.*

One of a pair of line engravings. 3⅞ in. by 7¾ in. Colored by hand. ☆ Stauffer 87.

130

Second View of Com. Perry's Victory. ☆ *M. Corne p. W. B. Annin Sc.* ☆ *Engraved for The Naval Monument* ☆ *Copy right 1815.*

The second of a pair of line engravings. 3⅞ in. by 7¾ in. Colored by hand. ☆ Stauffer 88.

ABOVE PAIR OF ENGRAVINGS LENT BY IRVING S. OLDS.

131

Battle of Erie, 1ˢᵗ. View ☆ *I. Sanford Sc.*

132

Battle of Erie, 2ⁿᵈ. View ☆ *I. Sanford Sc.*

Pair of line engravings printed on the same page. Each 3¼ in. by 5¹³⁄₁₆ in. In black and white. ☆ Stauffer 2742.

ABOVE PAIR OF ENGRAVINGS LENT BY HENRY O. HAVEMEYER.

133

Perry's Victory, above a view of Perry transferring his flag to the *Niagara*. Under the view: *For Free trade & Sailors Rights The Columbian Seaman fights And his Watchword Dont Surrender the Ship.* ☆ *Chiquet Sc. N. Y.* ☆ Undated.

Line and roulette engraving. 3 in. by 5¼ in. In black and white. ☆ Fielding 295.

LENT BY HALL PARK MCCULLOUGH.

Chiquet is believed to have been a French engraver, who for a short time did engraving work in New York.

134

Battle of Lake Erie, taken 15 Minutes after the commencement of the action. Statement follows indicating names and positions of the ships of the British and American fleets with their armament. ☆ *J. Evans, pinxᵗ. On Stone by T. S. Wagner.* ☆ *P. S. Duval, Lith. Philᵃ.* ☆ *U. S. Military Magazine Army & Navy. Vol. 2* ☆ *Entered according to act of Congress in the Year 1840, by Huddy & Duval, in the Clerk's Office of the District Court of the Eastern District of Pennᵃ.*

One of a pair of lithographs. 7⅜ in. by 11⅛ in. Colored by hand.

135

Battle of Lake Erie. Perry Victorious closing Scene of the action. Statement follows indicating names and positions of the ships of the British and American fleets with their armament. ☆ *J. Evans, pinxᵗ. On Stone by J. Queen. P. S. Duval, Lith. Philᵃ.* ☆ *U. S. Military Magazine—Army and Navy. Vol. 2ⁿᵈ* ☆ *Entered according to act of Congress in the year 1840. by Huddy & Duval in the Clerk's Office of the District Court of the Eastern District of Pᵃ.*

The second of a pair of lithographs. 7⁵⁄₁₆ in. by 10¼ in. Colored by hand.

THE ABOVE PAIR OF LITHOGRAPHS LENT BY IRVING S. OLDS.

136

Naval Heroes of the United States. Nᵒ. 1. Battle of Lake Erie. ☆ Oval portraits of *Oliver H. Perry, James Lawrence, Stephen Decatur, David Porter, Johnston Blakeley* and *William Bainbridge* around view of Battle of Lake Erie in center. ☆ *Lith. & Pub by N. Currier, 2 Spruce St. N. Y.* ☆ *Entered according to Act of Congress in the year 1846 by N. Currier, in the Clerk's office of the District Court of the Southern District of N. Y.*

Lithograph. 9¼ in. by 12¼ in. Colored by hand. ☆ H. T. Peters's Currier & Ives 1936.

LENT BY IRVING S. OLDS.

137

Perry's Victory. ☆ Artist, lithographer and publisher not named. ☆ Undated.

Lithograph. 7½ in. by 10⅜ in. Colored by hand.

LENT BY IRVING S. OLDS.

138

Perry's Victory On Lake Erie. Fought Sept͏ʳ. 10ᵗʰ. 1813. ☆ *This plate represents the position of the two Fleets, at the moment when the Niagara is pushing through the enemy's line, pouring her thunder upon them from both broadsides, and forcing them to surrender in succession to the American Flag, Commodore Perry, having a short time before left the Lawrence in a small boat, amidst a tremendous fire from the British squadron, and hoisted his Flag on board the Niagara. "We have met the enemy and they are ours." Com: O. H. Perry. Lawrence, killed & wounded 83.* ☆ *Lith: & Pub: by N. Currier, 2 Spruce Sͭ. N. Y. Signed N. Sarony.* ☆ *Undated.*

Lithograph. 8 in. by 12½ in. Colored by hand. ☆ H. T. Peters's Currier & Ives 1138.

LENT BY HARRY T. PETERS.

139

Perry's Victory on Lake Erie. Fought Sepͭ. 10ᵗʰ 1813. Lawrence killed & wounded 88 A description of the action follows identical in language with that contained on the above described lithograph by N. Currier. Names of the *Lawrence* and the *Niagara* below the view. ☆ *Lithᵒ. & Pubᵈ. by J. Baillie 118 Nassau Sͭ N. Y. & by J. Soule New Bedford Mass.* ☆ Undated.

Lithograph. 7¹³⁄₁₆ in. by 12⅜ in. Colored by hand.

LENT BY ESTATE OF FRANCIS P. GARVAN.

140

Perry's Victory on Lake Erie. Fought Septͬ. 10ᵗʰ 1813. A description of the action follows identical in language with that contained on the above described lithograph by N. Currier. ☆ *Kellogg & Thayer, 144 Fulton St, N. Y. E. B. & E. C. Kellogg; 136 Main St, Hartford Conn. B. Needham, 233 Main St, Buffalo.* ☆ Undated.

Lithograph. 7⅞ in. by 12⅜ in. Colored by hand. ☆ H. T. Peters states in *America On Stone* that Kellogg & Thayer had an office at 144 Fulton St, N. Y. during 1846–47.

141

Battle on Lake Erie. Commodore Perry captured the British fleet under Commodore Barclay, after a severe action, September 10th. 1813. ☆ Artist and engraver not named. ☆ Undated. Printed with an engraving of "Battle of Plattsburg" on a single sheet.

Line engraving. 2⅛ in. by 2⅝ in. In black and white.

142

Historical chintz, inscribed *War Declared Against Great Britain June 12 1812 First Naval Victory Augt. 19 1812. Since which Period until the Signing of the Preliminaries of Peace at Ghent on the 24 Decr. 1814 We Have Taken 1056 Vessels. Huzza Huzza* ☆ Contains oval panel inscribed *Brilliant Naval Victory on Lake Erie Sepr. 15 1814,* with smaller panel below inscribed *Glorious Victory on Lake Champlain Sepr. 15 1814.* At the sides are smaller oval panels of the engagements between the *Constitution* and *Guerrière, Wasp* and *Frolic, United States* and *Macedonian, Constitution* and *Java, Hornet* and *Peacock,* and *Enterprise* and *Boxer.* Medallion portraits of Perry and Macdonough beside the center inscription. Signing of the Treaty of Peace at Ghent on Decr. 24, 1814 is shown at the bottom.

Size of chintz: 28¾ in. by 30⅝ in. In color.

There are somewhat similar historical chintzes of other American naval actions.

GENERAL PIKE AND WOLF
SEPTEMBER 28, 1813

Commodore Chauncey and his fleet returned to Sackett's Harbor on Lake Ontario after the capture of Fort George on May 27, 1813 and the contemporaneous raid on that base by a British squadron taking advantage of the American fleet's absence. Chauncey chose to remain at Sackett's Harbor until the completion of the new sloop-of-war *General Pike,* which he hoped would give him an equality with the naval force of Sir James Yeo. This ship was finished toward the end of July 1813. During the following three months there were frequent partial conflicts between the British and American squadrons on Lake Ontario, neither side seeming willing to risk a fought-out decision.

One such inconclusive encounter took place on September 28, 1813, when the two fleets met, the *General Pike* engaging for a time the British sloop-of-war *Wolf* in the center of the enemy's line. The English fleet was able to outsail Commodore Chauncey's squadron and escaped.

143

A Scene on Lake Ontario. (above the view) ☆ *United States Sloop of War Gen. Pike, Commodore Chauncey and the British Sloop of War Wolf, sir James Yeo, Preparing for action Sep^t. 28th. 1813.* ☆ *R. Rawdon Sc.* ☆ *Published and Sold by Shelton & Kensett Cheshire Con. Novem^r. 1st. 1813.*

Line engraving. 8¼ in. by 14⅛ in. Colored by hand.

LENT BY H. WUNDERLICH AND O. M. TORRINGTON.

RALPH RAWDON in 1813 was engaged in the engraving business at Cheshire, Conn., in association with Thomas Kensett. About 1816, he moved to Albany, N. Y., where he engraved stipple portraits. In that city he conducted a bank-note and general engraving business in partnership with Asaph Willard.

144

South-east view of Sackett's harbour. Positions of forts, blockhouses and contonments indicated below. ☆ *T. Birch del. W. Strickland sc.* ☆ Undated.

Line engraving. 3¹³⁄₁₆ in. by 7⁹⁄₁₆ in. In black and white.

LENT BY HENRY O. HAVEMEYER.

CAPTURE OF THE ESSEX
MARCH 28, 1814

When the *Constitution* and the *Hornet* carried their cruise to the South Atlantic in the latter part of 1812, it was the expectation of Commodore Bainbridge that his two ships would be joined off the east coast of South America by the frigate *Essex*, 32 guns, Captain David Porter. This meeting failed, so the *Essex* went on around Cape Horn into the Pacific, the first American man-of-war to enter that ocean.

For six months Captain Porter cruised around the eastern Pacific in the vicinity of the Galapagos Islands. He broke up the enemy's whaling fleet in that region, capturing twelve British whalers and driving those remaining into port. The only source of supplies for the *Essex* was her prizes. After extensive overhauling at the Marquesas Islands, which Porter took possession of in the name of the United States, the *Essex* sailed in December 1813 with her consort, the *Essex-Junior*, an armed prize, in search of further prizes, finally proceeding to Valparaiso.

Reports of these losses in the Pacific led the British to send out a strong squadron to seek the *Essex*. Two vessels of this squadron, the frigate *Phoebe*, Captain James Hillyar, and the sloop-of-war *Cherub*, Captain Tucker, arrived at Valparaiso on February 8, 1814, and for more than six weeks blockaded the *Essex* and *Essex-Junior* in that port. Captain Porter failed in his repeated efforts to bring about a single-ship action between the *Essex* and the *Phoebe*, two vessels of about equal strength.

On March 28, 1814 the *Essex* sought to escape, but immediately ran into a heavy squall which carried away her main topmast. When the *Phoebe* and the *Cherub* gave chase, Captain Porter attempted to regain Valparaiso to repair the damage to his ship. Failing in this, he anchored near shore in neutral waters, where he was immediately attacked by the two British ships. Although unable effectively to use his broadsides while at anchor, Captain Porter crippled the *Cherub*, forcing her to haul off. He then cut the cable of the *Essex* with the intention of closing with the *Phoebe* and boarding her. This ship, however, by reason of the disabled state of the American frigate, was able to choose the distance which best suited her long guns. Being unable to close, Captain Porter tried to beach his ship and land the crew. The wind suddenly shifted and exposed the *Essex* to a raking fire from her opponent. The *Essex* was afire and unmanageable; most of her officers had been lost; many of her guns had been disabled; the *Phoebe* was able to aim at her as at a target. After a desperate struggle of nearly two and a half hours, Captain Porter gave the painful order to strike his colors.

The extraordinary cruise of the *Essex* reflected great glory upon the American navy, even though it terminated in the capture of that illustrious

[83]

frigate. It has been said that to David Porter was granted greatness in defeat. One of Porter's midshipmen on the *Essex* was David G. Farragut.

145

Capture of the Essex ☆ *Neele & Son, sc. Strand* ☆ Artist and publisher not named. ☆ Undated. Apparently intended for book illustration as print is marked *N°. 47.*

Line engraving. 3⅞ in. by 7¹⁄₁₆ in. In black and white.

LENT BY HENRY O. HAVEMEYER.

146

Capture of The Essex ☆ *M. Corne, p. A. Bowen, sc.* ☆ Undated.

Woodcut. 3¼ in. by 6¹³⁄₁₆ in. In black and white.

A similar woodcut, inscribed "Capture of The Essex," without the names of Corne and Bowen, is used as an illustration in Bowen's *The Naval Monument*, published in 1816.

LENT BY HENRY O. HAVEMEYER.

147

Contemporaneous water-color painting inscribed: *28 March. His Majesty's Ship Phoebe engaging the American Frigate Essex off Valparaiso, South America, 1814.* ☆ Artist not named. ☆ Undated.

6⅜ in. by 10⅞ in.

LENT BY H. WUNDERLICH AND O. M. TORRINGTON.

PEACOCK AND L'EPERVIER
APRIL 29, 1814

The effectiveness of the British blockade of American Atlantic ports prevented most of our ships from getting to sea in 1814. One which so succeeded was the new sloop-of-war *Peacock*, 22 guns, under the command of Captain Lewis Warrington, which stole past the blockade off New York on March 12, 1814. This vessel had been named for the British brig of the same name captured by James Lawrence a year before.

On April 29, 1814, the *Peacock* attacked the British brig *L'Epervier*, 18 guns, Captain Richard Wales, off the coast of Florida, while the latter was engaged in convoying three merchantmen. The foreyard of the *Peacock* was hit at the first fire, disabling the fore and fore-topsail and seriously hampering the maneuverability of the ship. This compelled Captain Warrington to rely entirely upon his gunfire. He first endeavored to cripple the rigging of the enemy. When the British brig had lost her head sails and her main boom had fallen upon the wheel, the *Peacock* hauled close under her opponent's lee and poured a hot fire against her hull. At the end of a struggle of forty-five minutes, *L'Epervier* struck her colors. Two were wounded on the *Peacock*, whose hull was unhit. *L'Epervier* had eight killed and fifteen wounded.

148

Peacock and L'Epervier ☆ *T. Birch del. W. Strickland sc.* ☆ Undated.

Aquatint. 3⅜ in. by 6 in. Colored by hand. ☆ Stauffer 3060.

LENT BY IRVING S. OLDS.

149

[Peacock and L'Epervier] Title in pencil. ☆ *Hamlin Aq^t.* ☆ Undated.

Aquatint. 3½ in. by 5⅞ in. Colored by hand. ☆ Proof before title. ☆ Stauffer 1246.

LENT BY HALL PARK MCCULLOUGH.

150

The Peacock And Epervier ☆ *T. Birch, del. A. Bowen, sc.* ☆ Undated.

Woodcut. 3⁵⁄₁₆ in. by 6¹¹⁄₁₆ in. Colored by hand.

LENT BY ESTATE OF FRANCIS P. GARVAN.

A similar woodcut, inscribed "The Peacock And Epervier", without the names of Corne and Bowen, is used an an illustration in Bowen's *The Naval Monument*, published in 1816.

ATTACK ON FORT OSWEGO
MAY 6, 1814

Newly constructed vessels temporarily gave the British a naval superiority on Lake Ontario during the early part of 1814.

On May 5, 1814, a British force, consisting of 3 ships, 2 brigs, 2 schooners and a number of gunboats, commanded by Sir James Yeo, appeared off Fort Oswego on the southern shore of the lake. The landing of the British force was severely contested, but on the following day the British succeeded in occupying the place and in capturing a quantity of naval stores. Commodore Chauncey's official report states that Sir James Yeo's losses were 70 killed and 165 wounded or missing.

Fort Oswego was evacuated by the British on May 8, 1814, after the barracks had been set on fire. A month later the growing strength of the fleet of Commodore Chauncey caused Sir James Yeo to give up his blockade of Sackett's Harbor and to retire to his base at Kingston.

151

Attack on Fort Oswego, Lake Ontario, N. America. May 6th. 1814, Noon. Dedicated to His Majesty's Royal Marine Forces, and those employ'd on the Expedition. Plate 1. References below the print to fort, boats, position of troops, etc. ☆ *Drawn by I. Hewett, Lt. Royal Marines. Engrav'd by R. Havell.* ☆ *London, Published May 1, 1815.*

One of a pair of aquatints. 15⅝ in. by 21⅞ in. Colored by hand.

152

Storming Fort Oswego, by 2nd. Battalion Royal Marines and a party of Seamen: 15m. past Twelve at Noon. Plate 2. Dedicated to His Majesty's Royal Marine Forces, and those employ'd on the Expedition. References below the print to the boats and troops involved. ☆ *Drawn by I. Hewett Lieut Royal Marines. Engraved by R. Havell.* ☆ *London, Published May 1, 1815.*

The second of a pair of aquatints. 15½ in. by 21⅜ in. Colored by hand. ☆ Parker 237–a.

ABOVE PAIR OF AQUATINTS LENT BY IRVING S. OLDS.

153

Attack on Fort Oswego, on Lake Ontario, North America. May 6ᵗʰ. 1814. ☆ *Drawn by Captⁿ. Steele. Engraved by R. Havell & Son.* ☆ *Published April 8ᵗʰ. 1817, for the Proprietor, by R. Havell, 3, Chapel Street, Tottenham Court Road.*

One of a pair of aquatints. 10⅞ in. by 15¾ in. Colored by hand.

154

Storming Fort Oswego, on Lake Ontario, North America. May 6ᵗʰ. 1814. ☆ *Drawn by Captⁿ. Steele. Engraved by R. Havell & Son.* ☆ *Published April 8ᵗʰ. 1817, for the Proprietor, by R. Havell, 3, Chapel Street, Tottenham Court Road.*

The second of a pair of aquatints. 11 in. by 15¾ in. Colored by hand.

ABOVE PAIR OF AQUATINTS LENT BY IRVING S. OLDS.

155

Attack on Fort Oswego. ☆ *W. Strickland sc.* ☆ Undated.

Aquatint. 3¾ in. by 7⁷⁄₁₆ in. In black and white. ☆ Stauffer 3057.

LENT BY HENRY O. HAVEMEYER.

156

A View of the Fort & Harbour of Oswego from Lake Ontario Representing the Attack by the British on the 6ᵗʰ. of May 1814 ☆ *T. H. Wentworth del.*

Line engraving. 3⅝ in. by 7¹⁵⁄₁₆ in. In black and white. ☆ From *The American Magazine, 1816* ☆ Fielding 1861.

LENT BY HENRY O. HAVEMEYER.

WASP AND REINDEER
JUNE 28, 1814

The *Wasp*, 22 guns, was the third of the new American sloops-of-war to get by the British blockade and seek enemy ships on the high seas. Under the command of Master Commandant Johnston Blakeley, the *Wasp* sailed from Portsmouth, N. H., on May 1, 1814, and headed directly for the English Channel, where several captures were made.

On June 28, 1814, Blakeley came on the British brig *Reindeer*, 19 guns, Captain R. William Manners. A severe action ensued at close range. Serious damage to the *Reindeer* caused Captain Manners to attempt to turn the tide of battle by boarding the *Wasp*. Captain Manners was killed while leading his boarders. This attack being repelled, Blakeley called upon his own men to board. This act was successfully accomplished and the flag of the British ship was hauled down half an hour after the first shot had been fired by the *Reindeer*.

The severity of the engagement is indicated by the losses. Out of a crew of 173, the *Wasp* had eleven killed and fifteen wounded; her opponent, twenty-five killed and forty-two wounded, more than one-half of the ship's company. The *Reindeer* was badly cut to pieces, and, after all prisoners had been removed, Captain Blakely gave orders for his prize to be burned.

Subsequently, the career of the *Wasp* was tragic. Refitted at L'Orient, she continued her career of destruction of British shipping. After forcing the British brig *Avon* to surrender in a fierce engagement on the night of September 1, 1814, the *Wasp* was obliged to abandon her prize (which later sank) by the arrival on the scene of three additional British men-of-war. The *Wasp* then proceeded past Lisbon and Madeira into the South Atlantic, where she completely disappeared, never being heard from after mid-October. During her cruise the *Wasp* had captured or destroyed fifteen enemy merchantmen.

157

The Wasp And Reindeer. ☆ *M. Corne, p. A. Bowen, sc.* ☆ Undated.

Woodcut. 3¼ in. by 6¹³⁄₁₆ in. In black and white.

LENT BY HENRY O. HAVEMEYER.

158

The Wasp And Avon. ☆ *M. Corne, p. A. Bowen, sc.*

Woodcut. 3¼ in. by 6¹³⁄₁₆ in. In black and white.

LENT BY HENRY O. HAVEMEYER.

Two similar woodcuts, inscribed "The Wasp and Reindeer" and "The Wasp And Avon", without the names of Corne and Bowen, are used as illustrations in Bowen's *The Naval Monument*, published in 1816.

BATTLE OF LAKE CHAMPLAIN
(BATTLE OF PLATTSBURG)
SEPTEMBER 11, 1814

England's program in 1814 for the successful termination of the War of 1812 included an invasion into the United States from Canada by way of Lake Champlain. Veteran troops were sent from Europe for this purpose. For the consummation of such a plan complete naval control of Lake Champlain was essential.

Commodore Thomas Macdonough had charge of the American end of a shipbuilding race on the lake. When his fleet was ready, he took up a position at Plattsburg, which would give him command of the lake so long as he could remain there.

Following the launching of a powerful addition to the British naval force, the frigate *Confiance* of 37 guns, Governor General Sir George Prevost set out on August 31, 1814, on the march for Plattsburg, with an army of more than ten thousand men, mostly trained soldiers from the Napoleonic wars. By September 4, 1814, this British force had occupied Plattsburg, the weaker American army under General Alexander Macomb withdrawing to high land across the nearby Saranac River. Prevost then waited at Plattsburg for the arrival of the British fleet commanded by Commodore George Downie, whose departure was temporarily held up awaiting final completion of the *Confiance*.

On the morning of September 11, 1814, the British fleet, consisting of a frigate, a brig, two sloops-of-war and thirteen galleys, approached Plattsburg and found Macdonough's squadron at anchor off shore in battle line, prepared to resist their further advance. Macdonough's force was composed of a ship of 26 guns, a brig of 20 guns, a schooner of 17 guns, a sloop-of-war of 7 guns and ten galleys. The total weight of broadside fire of the two fleets was about equal. General Prevost and his troops did not attempt to force the American ships out into the lake where the more powerful *Confiance* and the longer range guns of the British fleet could be used to the best advantage.

The flagship *Confiance*, with an inexperienced crew unused to their ship, got ahead of the balance of the outspread British line and at the outset received the concentrated fire of the American fleet. Commodore Downie was killed early in the battle. After two hours of hard fighting, largely carried on by the flagship *Saratoga* and the *Eagle*, the two largest ships of Macdonough's force, the *Confiance* and her companion, the brig *Linnet*, surrendered. Previously, one of the British sloops had been captured and the other ran ashore. The British galleys were sunk or dispersed. At the end of the action, there was not a mast in either squadron that could stand to make sail on.

While the engagement was in progress, the British land forces bombarded General Macomb's position and attempted an advance, which was repulsed.

When Governor General Prevost became aware of the completeness of the American naval victory, he immediately marched his veteran army back to Canada. He could not go forward on the proposed invasion with Lake Champlain indisputably in American hands.

Captain Dudley W. Knox in his History of the United States Navy states: "Commodore Macdonough's dynamic energy, inspiring leadership, skillful dispositions and superb courage had won a victory afloat which decided the war."

159

Macdonough's Victory on Lake Champlain, and Defeat of the British Army at Plattsburg by Genl. Macomb, Septr. 11th. 1814. ☆ *Painted by H. Reinagle. Engraved by B. Tanner.* ☆ Undated.

Line engraving. $16^{15}/_{16}$ in. by $24\frac{1}{2}$ in. Colored by hand. ☆ Possibly a first state before publication and entry lines were added.

This engraving was published with an engraved key and plan of the battle, both of which are included in this exhibition as Nos. 159–a and 159–b. ☆ Stauffer 3134.

Illustrated

LENT BY IRVING S. OLDS.

Another state of this engraving was issued with the following publication data: *Published 4th July 1816 by B. Tanner engraver N°. 74 South Eighth Street Philadelphia. Printed by Rogers and Esler. Entered according to Act of Congress the 22nd. day of May 1816; by Benjamin Tanner of the state of Pennsylvania.*

There are two other states of this print. This is a companion piece to Benjamin Tanner's engravings of "United States and Macedonian" and "Battle of Lake Erie".

BATTLE OF LAKE CHAMPLAIN, SEPTEMBER 11, 1814

Engraved by Benjamin Tanner after a painting by Hugh Reinagle

(See No. 159)

159a

Small water-color painting of the Battle of Lake Champlain, believed to be a sketch painted by Hugh Reinagle.

5⅞ in. by 7⅞ in.

LENT BY IRVING S. OLDS.

HUGH REINAGLE (1790–1834) was a well known American painter. He studied painting under John Joseph Holland. His work includes several New York views. He worked in both water colors and oils. Reinagle was one of the fifteen founders of the National Academy of Design.

160

Naval Action on Lake Champlain. Read sc. ☆ Undated.

Line engraving. 3¹³⁄₁₆ in. by 7¾ in. Colored by hand. ☆ Stauffer 2659.

LENT BY ESTATE OF FRANCIS P. GARVAN.

161

Battle of Plattsburg. ☆ *Read sc.* ☆ Undated.

Line engraving. 3⅞ in. by 7¹³⁄₁₆ in. Colored by hand. ☆ Stauffer 2660.

LENT BY ESTATE OF FRANCIS P. GARVAN.

A similar engraving in black and white, owned by Hall Park McCullough, bears the additional inscription: "Printed by Samˡ. Maverick N. Y."

162

Com. Macdonough's Victory on Lake Champlain. Sepʳ. 11ᵗʰ. 1814. ☆ *M. Corné p. W. Hoogland Sc.* ☆ *Engraved for The Naval Monument* ☆ *Entered according to act of Congress Nov. 25ᵗʰ. 1815 by A. Bowen.*

Line engraving. 3⅞ in. by 7¹⁵⁄₁₆ in. In black and white.

LENT BY HENRY O. HAVEMEYER.

163

Battle of Plattsburg. On the 11th. of September 1814, Commodore Macdonough captured the British fleet on Lake Champlain, while Gen. Macomb repulsed the land forces of the enemy. ☆ *Artist and engraver not named.* ☆ Undated. Printed with an engraving of "Battle of Lake Erie" on a single sheet.

Line engraving. 2⅛ in. by 2⅝ in. In black and white.

LENT BY HENRY O. HAVEMEYER.

164

Battle of Plattsburg Bay Mᶜ.Donough's Victory. Sepᵗ. 11ᵗʰ 1814. ☆ *On Stone by Jaˢ. Queen. P. S. Duval, Lith. Philᵃ.* ☆ *U. S. Military Magazine. Army & Navy. Vol 2ⁿᵈ* ☆ *Entered according to Act of Congress in the Year 1840, by Huddy & Duval, in the Clerk's Office of the District Court of the Eastern District of Pensylvᵃ.*

Lithograph. 7⅜ in. by 10⅞ in. Colored by hand.

LENT BY HENRY O. HAVEMEYER.

165

Naval Heroes of the United States. Nº. 2. Battle of Lake Champlain. Oval portraits of *Thomas Macdonough, Isaac Hull, Charles Stewart, Wm. Henry Allen, Jacob Jones,* and *Joshua Barney* around view of Battle of Lake Champlain in center. ☆ *Lith. & Pub. by N. Currier, 2 Spruce St N. Y.* ☆ *Entered according to Act of Congress in the year 1846 by N. Currier, in the Clerk's office of the District Court of the Southern District of N. Y.*

Lithograph. 9 in. by 12¼ in. Colored by hand. ☆ H. T. Peters' Currier & Ives 1937.

LENT BY IRVING S. OLDS.

166

M'Donough's Victʸ. On Lake Champlain. Statement follows of the armament and losses of the two fleets. ☆ *Lith. & Pub. by N. Currier, 2 Spruce St. N. Y.* ☆ *Entered according to Act of Congress in the year 1846 by N. Currier, in the Clerk's office of the District Court of the Southern District of N. Y.*

Lithograph. 7¾ in. by 12¾ in. Colored by hand. ☆ H. T. Peters' Currier & Ives 1137.

LENT BY IRVING S. OLDS.

167

M'Donough's Victory On Lake Champlain. After an Action of 2 Hours, 2 Minutes. Statement follows of the number of vessels, armament and losses of the two fleets. ☆ Different view from that shown in the foregoing print. ☆ *Pub. by N. Currier, 2 Spruce St. N. Y.* ☆ *Entered according to Act of Congress A.D. 1846, by N. Currier, in the Clerk's Office of the Dist. Court of the Southⁿ. Dist. of N. York.*

Lithograph. 8 in. by 12½ in. Colored by hand.

LENT BY IRVING S. OLDS.

168

M'Donough's Victory on Lake Champlain. After an Action of 2 hours, & 2 Minutes. Statement follows of number of vessels, armament and losses of the American and British forces. ☆ Lithographer and publisher not named. ☆ Undated.

Lithograph. 8 in. by 12½ in. Colored by hand.

LENT BY HENRY O. HAVEMEYER.

169

Title page: *The Analectic Magazine July to December 1818. ☆ C. H. Parker script. et Sculpsit ☆ Small oval engraved view in center of page, inscribed Comr. Macdonough's Farm-House, on Cumberland bay, Lake Champlain. in the Diste. are the American Forts, Town of Plattsburg, River Saranac, the British Camp & headqrs. of Sr. Geo. Provost. ☆ Philadelphia Published by M. Thomas Johnson's Head No. 52 Chestnut St.*

Line engraving. Oval view, 1⅞ in. by 3½ in. In black and white.

LENT BY ROBERT FRIDENBERG.

170

McDonough Pointing The Gun. Battle of Lake Champlain. ☆ J. R. Chapin. F. F. Walker ☆ Virtue & Yorston, New York.

Line engraving. 5¼ in. by 7⁷⁄₁₆ in. In black and white.

LENT BY ROBERT FRIDENBERG.

BOMBARDMENT OF FORT McHENRY
SEPTEMBER 13, 1814

After the burning of Washington in August 1814, the naval force which had accompanied the British troops moved up Chesapeake Bay toward Baltimore. Defences were erected near the city and hulks were sunk to obstruct the channel near Fort McHenry, two miles from Baltimore. Commodore John Rodgers brought a considerable force of marines and seamen to reinforce the American troops already at Baltimore.

On September 10, 1814, the British landed several thousand men about fourteen miles from Baltimore to act jointly with the naval force in an attack upon that city. The opposition proved to be too formidable and the expedition was abandoned a few days later.

The action at Fort McHenry, which was commanded by Major Armstead, is well described in the following extracts from the report of General Samuel Smith to the Secretary of War: "The enemy made his approach by water at the same time that his army was advancing on the land, and commenced a discharge of bombs and rockets at the fort as soon as he got within range of it. The situation of Major Armstead was peculiarly trying—the enemy having taken his position at such a distance as to render offensive operations on the part of the fort entirely fruitless, while their bombs and rockets were every moment falling in and about it—the officers and men being at the same time entirely exposed. The vessels, however, had the temerity to approach somewhat nearer—they were as soon compelled to withdraw. During the night, whilst the enemy on land was retreating, and whilst the bombardment was most severe, two or three rocket vessels and barges succeeded in getting up the Ferry Branch; but they were soon compelled to retire, by the forts in that quarter, commanded by Lieutenant Newcomb of the navy, and Lieutenant Webster of the flotilla. These forts also destroyed one of the barges, with all on board. The barges and battery at the Lazaretto, under the command of Lieutenant Rutter of the flotilla, kept up a brisk and it is believed a successful fire during the hottest period of the bombardment . . ."

The bombardment of Fort McHenry was the occasion for the composition of our national anthem, *The Star Spangled Banner*. Francis Scott Key, its author, witnessed the attack from on board an American flag-of-truce boat anchored near the British fleet.

171

A View of the Bombardment of Fort M^c. Henry, near Baltimore, by the British fleet, taken from the Observatory, under the Command of Admirals Cochrane, & Cockburn, on the morning of the 13th. of Sepr. 1814, which lasted 24 hours, & thrown from 1500 to 1800 shells, in the Night attempted to land by forcing a passage up the ferry branch but were repulsed with great loss. Table of references appears at right of title. ☆ *J. Bower sc. Phil^a.* ☆ *Copy Right Secured.*

Aquatint. 11 in. by 17⅛ in. In black and white. ☆ Stauffer 236.   *Illustrated*

LENT BY ESTATE OF FRANCIS P. GARVAN.

JOHN BOWER was an engraver at Philadelphia during the period from 1810 to 1819. In addition to the aquatint of the Bombardment of Fort McHenry, Bower

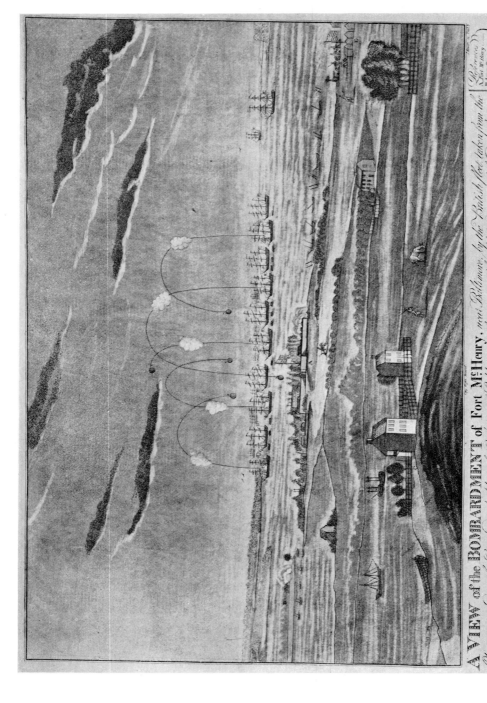

BOMBARDMENT OF FORT McHENRY, SEPTEMBER 13, 1814

Engraved by John Bower

(See No. 171)

engraved maps, stipple portraits of Washington and John Adams, and plates for Collins's *Quarto Bible*, 3rd Edition, 1814, and Bunyan's *Pilgrims Progress*, published at Philadelphia in 1817.

172

Bombardment of Fort McHenry. ☆ *W. Strickland del. W. Kneass Sc.* ☆ Undated. Line engraving. 4⅛ in. by 8⅛ in. Colored by hand. ☆ Stauffer 1658.

LENT BY ESTATE OF FRANCIS P. GARVAN.

173

Bombardment of Fort McHenry 1814. ☆ *Aquatinted by J. Hill* ☆ Proof before all letters. ☆ Undated.

Line engraving. 13⅝ in. by 19⅝ in. In black and white.

LENT BY ROBERT FRIDENBERG.

JOHN HILL (1770–1850) had a successful career as an engraver in aquatint. Born in London, Hill commenced his engraving work in that metropolis, where he made a number of views after paintings by J. M. W. Turner and others. Coming to the United States in 1816, Hill established himself in Philadelphia, after a short stay in New York. Hill later returned to New York, where he lived from 1824 until 1839. Hill is best known for his series of large aquatint plates of American scenery, after paintings by Joshua Shaw, for *The Land Scape Album*, published in Philadelphia in 1820 by Hill and Shaw, and for his aquatints of views along the Hudson River after paintings by William G. Wall, published in the *Hudson River Port Folio*. He also issued American drawing-books with colored plates.

ATTACK ON THE AMERICAN PRIVATEER
GENERAL ARMSTRONG AT FAYAL
SEPTEMBER 26, 1814

The American privateer *General Armstrong*, Captain Samuel Chester Reid, escaped the blockade off Sandy Hook on September 9, 1814, and came to anchor seventeen days later in Fayal Roads in the Azores. That evening the British 74-gun ship-of-the-line *Plantagenet*, Captain Robert Lloyd, the 38-gun frigate *Rota* and the 18-gun brig *Carnation* entered the same waters.

These ships were a part of the British fleet carrying troops across the Atlantic for an attack on New Orleans.

During the night twelve or more boats from the British squadron, carrying in the neighborhood of four hundred men, attacked the *General Armstrong*. At the end of a bitter fight of forty minutes, the surviving small boats retired, the British attempt to board the privateer having been repulsed. The British losses amounted to 173 killed and wounded.

The following day the *Carnation* closed in and opened fire on the *General Armstrong*. Before scuttling and abandoning his ship, Captain Reid succeeded in seriously damaging the rigging of his adversary.

This engagement proved to be of great significance, as it resulted in the British squadron being detained in the harbor for a week, a delay which provided indispensable time to General Andrew Jackson for perfecting the defense of New Orleans.

174

The American Privateer "General Armstrong" Capt. Sam. C. Reid. In the Harbor of Fayol (Azores) Oct^r. *26*th. *1814. Repulsing the attack of 14 boats containing 400 men from the British Ships Plantagenet 74 Rota 44 and Carnation 18 Guns. The General Armstrong was 246 tons burthen Carried 6 Nine pounders and a Long Tom (42 pounder,) amid ships and a crew of 90 men. The British loss was 120 killed and 132 wounded — Americans lost 2 killed and 7 wounded. ☆ Lith. and Pub. by N. Currier 152 Nassau Street. N. Y.*

Lithograph. 8 in. by 12⅝ in. Colored by hand. ☆ H. T. Peters' Currier & Ives 1132.

LENT BY IRVING S. OLDS.

ATTACK ON THE AMERICAN GUNBOATS IN
LAKE BORGNE, LA.
DECEMBER 14, 1814

General Andrew Jackson first established his land force at Mobile, Ala., toward the end of 1814, believing that would be the initial objective of the British in their effort to capture New Orleans.

A small American squadron to oppose the enemy had been assembled at

New Orleans under Commodore Daniel T. Patterson. It consisted of a sloop-of-war, two schooners, five gunboats, and a tender. Patterson predicted that the British would advance directly on New Orleans by way of Lake Borgne. This proved to be their actual plan of campaign.

General Jackson arrived at New Orleans from Mobile early in December 1814. Six days later the British fleet, bringing the troops which had previously attacked Washington and Baltimore, with reinforcements taken on at Jamaica, anchored in the vicinity. The whole American army had not yet reached New Orleans and further time was needed, as much remained to be done to provide adequate defences.

The British had to transport their soldiers in small boats for about sixty miles through shallow water. This appproach to New Orleans was defended by a major part of Commodore Patterson's squadron under the command of Lieutenant Thomas Ap. Catesby Jones.

On December 13, 1814, one hundred and six barges, carrying about 1000 British troops, left their fleet for the advance on New Orleans. The next morning they encountered in Lake Borgne Jones' small squadron, consisting mostly of gunboats. A bitterly contested engagement of two hours ensued, at the end of which six of the seven craft under Lieutenant Jones had been captured by the overwhelming British force to which they were opposed.

Despite this defeat, the American naval force had delayed the British advance for nine days. This delay, together with the aid furnished a few days later by Commodore Patterson's guns from the sloop *Louisiana* and his seamen from the schooner *Carolina*, were unquestionably material factors in General Jackson's decisive defeat of General Sir Edward Pakenham at New Orleans on January 8, 1815.

175

The Gallant Attack & Capture of the American Gun Boats in Lake Borgne by the Boats of the Squadron under the Command of Captain N. Lockyer. C. B. to whom & the Brave Officers & Seaman, this Representation is most respectfully dedicated by T. M. Williams R. N. ☆ Drawn by Lieut^t*. T. M. Williams. Printed by C. Hullmandel.*

Lithograph. $8^{15}/_{16}$ in. by $14\frac{1}{8}$ in. Colored by hand.

Reproduced as an illustration in Bowen's *The Sea. Its History and Romance.*

LENT BY ESTATE OF FRANCIS P. GARVAN.

PRESIDENT AND ENDYMION
JANUARY 15, 1815

On the night of January 14, 1815 the frigate *President*, 44 guns, under the command of Captain Stephen Decatur, slipped out of New York Harbor in the midst of a gale. The program was for the *President*, in company with the *Hornet*, *Peacock* and *Tom Bowline*, sailing singly from the United States, to rendezvous at the Island of Tristan d'Acuna in the South Atlantic, and then cruise in the Indian Ocean, hoping to emulate the success of the *Essex* in the Pacific. Unfortunately, the *President*, in leaving New York, grounded on a bar and sustained substantial damage to her hull and rudder braces. The adverse wind prevented her return to port.

Early the next morning, Decatur discovered four ships in chase of him, constituting the British blockading squadron under Captain John Hayes. In an effort to get away, Decatur threw overboard his small boats, cables, anchors and some of the supplies for the contemplated long cruise. The *President* was handicapped by the injuries sustained the night before. By late afternoon one vessel, the British frigate *Endymion*, 38 guns, Captain H. Hope, had approached within gunshot and opened fire, repeatedly reaching its mark. In this position, the *President* could not bring a single gun to bear. Decatur decided to try to capture the *Endymion*.

At dusk, Decatur altered his course for the purpose of bringing the enemy abeam. Although the *Endymion* kept off, the *President* was able at last to make use of her guns. Decatur hoped to disable his opponent before the other ships could arrive. A spirited action continued for two and a half hours, when the *Endymion*, badly injured, dropped out of the fight. The other British ships being in sight, Decatur could not follow the *Endymion* to finish the action. He resumed his original course in a further attempt to escape.

About midnight two of the pursuing frigates, each of 38 guns, with the *Majestic* not far behind, overhauled the *President*. Captain Decatur's official report states: " . . . two fresh ships of the enemy, the *Pomone* and *Tenedos*, had come up. The *Pomone* had opened her fire on the larboard bow, within musket shot; the other, about two cables' length astern, taking a raking position on our quarter; and the rest, with the exception of the *Endymion*, within gunshot. Thus situated, with about one-fifth of my crew killed and wounded, my ship crippled, and a more than fourfold force opposed to me, without a chance of escape left, I deemed it my duty to surrender." Captain Decatur gave up his sword to Captain Hayes, the commander of the British squadron, who promptly returned it. This action was fought after a treaty of peace had been signed at Ghent on December 24, 1814, news of which did not reach the United States for some weeks thereafter.

176

To the Captain, Officers and Brave Crew of His Majesty's Frigate — Endymion — as an Humble Record of British Skill, and Valour. — This Representation of the Gallant Action on the 15ᵗʰ day of January with the United States Ship — President — commanded by Commodore Decatur is Respectfully Inscribed by their most Obedientᵗ Servantᵗ, Thomas Rickards. Statement of the armament and crews of the two ships follows. ☆ *Drawn by an Officer of H.M.R.N.* ☆ *Hill Aquat.* ☆ *London, Published May 1–1815 by Thomas Rickards, 344, Strand:*

Aquatint. 14⅞ in. by 20⅞ in. Colored by hand.   *Illustrated*

LENT BY HENRY GRAVES, JR.

A second state of this print was published in 1838 by W. Deeley, Pentonville. There is also a third state without date or publication line.

177

To Captain H. Hope, the Officers, Seamen, and Marines, of His Majesty's Frigate, Endymion, This Print representing the Action with the American United States Frigate President, on Sunday Evening Janʸ. 15ᵗʰ. 1815. off Sandy Hook is respectfully Dedicated by their obedient humble Servants, J. Burr & G. Ballisat. Endymion 49 guns 345 men President 58 guns 525 men. difference 9 guns & 180 Men. ☆ *Painted by T. Buttersworth. Engraved by Joˢ. Jeakes.* ☆ *Published as the Act directs, June 1ˢᵗ. 1815, by J. Burr & G. Ballisat, Gracechurch Street, London.*

Aquatint. 15¾ in. by 21⅞ in. Colored by hand. ☆ Parker 238–a.

LENT BY ESTATE OF FRANCIS P. GARVAN.

178

To Captain H. Hope, the Officers, Seamen, and Marines of His Majesty's Frigate Endymion. This Print representing the Morning after the Action with the American United States Frigate, Presidentᵗ Janʸ. 16ᵗʰ. 1815 — which lasted two Hours and a half is respectfully Dedicated by their obedient Servants J. Burr & G. Ballisat. Endymion 12 Killed 14 Wounded Presidentᵗ 32 Killed 60 wounded, amongst the

ENGAGEMENT BETWEEN PRESIDENT AND ENDYMION, JANUARY 15, 1815   (See No. 176)

Aquatinted by John Hill after a drawing by an officer of the Royal Navy

former 1ˢᵗ. 3ᵈ. & 4ᵗʰ. Lieuᵗˢ. & 6 Midshipmen. Names of the five ships stated below the view. ☆ *Painted by T. Buttersworth. the particulars & the position of the Ships, by Lieuᵗ. Ormond of the Endymion. Engraved by J. Jeakes.* ☆ *Published as the Act directs June 1ˢᵗ 1815, by J. Burr & G. Ballisat. Gracechurch Street, London.*

Aquatint. 15⅝ in. by 21¼ in. Colored by hand. ☆ Parker 238–a.

LENT BY BEVERLEY R. ROBINSON.

The above described pair of aquatints were reissued in 1838.

179

The Capture of the U. S. Frigate, President, by a British Squadron, under the command of Commodore Hayes, off the Coast of America, January 1815. To Captain Henry Robinson, this print is respectfully dedicated by his sincere Friend Wᵐ. Skiddy Names of the five ships below the view. ☆ *Drawn & Lithᵈ by Samˡ. Walters, Gᵗ. George Sᵗ. Liverpool from a sketch by Capᵗ Wᵐ. Skiddy* ☆ *Day & Haghe Lithʳˢ to the Queen.*

Lithograph. 14¼ in. by 22⅝ in. Colored by hand.

LENT BY BEVERLEY R. ROBINSON.

180

A View of the Gallant Action between His Majestys Ship the Endymion and the United States Ship the President This Action was fought Janʸ. 15, 1815 when the Endymion Capᵗ. Hope after a contest of two hours and a half captured the President Comodore Decatur, she is one of the largest ships belonging to the United States She was taken off their own coast the Endymion had 11 Men killed and 14 Wounded the President about 100 killed and Wounded. Statement of force and armament of Endymion and President follows. ☆ Artist and engraver not named. ☆ *Published Febʸ. 24 1815 by J. Evans and Son Nᵒ. 42 Long Lane West Smithfield*

Line engraving. 12⅛ in. by 17⅜ in. Colored by hand.

LENT BY H. WUNDERLICH AND O. M. TORRINGTON.

181

The President Engaging The Endymion, While Pursued By The British Squadron. Position of the six ships indicated below the view. ☆ *M. Corne, p. A. Bowen, sc.* ☆ Undated.

Woodcut. 3¼ in. by 6¾ in. Colored by hand.

LENT BY ESTATE OF FRANCIS P. GARVAN.

A similar woodcut, inscribed "The President Engaging The Endymion, While Pursued By The British Squadron", without the names of Corne and Bowen, is used as an illustration in Bowen's *The Naval Monument*, published in 1816.

CONSTITUTION, LEVANT AND CYANE

FEBRUARY 20, 1815

This was another engagement fought after the signing of the treaty of peace at Ghent on Christmas eve, 1814.

The *Constitution*, now under the command of Captain Charles Stewart, managed to avoid the British blockade and got away from Boston on December 17, 1814. She had been held in that port since the previous April. A message was soon dispatched throughout the British fleet that the *Constitution* was again cruising. This famous frigate first sailed to Bermuda, where she made a capture, and then on to Madeira and the waters off Lisbon, adding an additional prize. On the afternoon of February 20, 1815, the *Constitution* observed two strange sails on the horizon off Madeira. Smaller British men-of-war had been sent out in pairs or more to intercept this much talked-of and feared American frigate.

The *Constitution* bore down to engage the two British ships, which proved to be the frigate *Cyane*, 34 guns, Captain Gordon Falcon, and the sloop-of-war *Levant*, 21 guns, Captain George Douglas. By masterful maneuvering, Captain Stewart delivered a staggering blow to the *Levant* and then dropped astern in a position to take on the more powerful *Cyane*. After forty-five minutes of heavy fire, the *Cyane* surrendered. The *Constitution* then set off in chase of the *Levant* and within two hours had overtaken her and made her a second prize. The *Constitution* suffered only trifling damage to her hull and rigging. She had four men killed and ten wounded.

About three weeks after the battle, a strong British squadron of three frigates under Sir George Collier forced the *Constitution* and her two prizes to put to sea from the harbor of Porto Praya, Island of San Jago, in the Cape Verde group. In an effort to escape, the three ships under the American flag separated. This strategy enabled the *Cyane* to get away unfollowed. Finally, the enemy squadron gave up the chase of the *Constitution* and concentrated on the *Levant*. She returned to port, where she was recaptured. The *Constitution* and the *Cyane* safely reached the United States.

This was a fitting climax to the truly remarkable fighting career of "Old Ironsides."

182

Capture of H. M. Ships Cyane & Levant, By The U. S. Frigate Constitution. To Chas. Stewart Esqr. His Officers & Crew. This Plate is most respectfully dedicated by Huddy & Duval: Position of the three ships, with their numbers of guns, indicated below the view. ☆ *From the Original Painting by Birch. On Stone by Ja^s. Queen.* ☆ *P. S. Duval Lith. Phil^a.* ☆ *U. S. Military Magazine. Army & Navy, N°. 6, Vol. 2nd*

Lithograph. 7 3/16 in. by 10 1/8 in. Colored by hand.

LENT BY ESTATE OF FRANCIS P. GARVAN.

183

The Constitution Taking The Cyane and Levant. ☆ Position of the three ships indicated below the view. ☆ *M. Corne, p. A. Anderson, sc.* ☆ Undated.

Woodcut. 3 1/4 in. by 6 11/16 in. Colored by hand.

LENT BY ESTATE OF FRANCIS P. GARVAN.

A similar woodcut, inscribed "The Constitution Taking The Cyane and Levant", without the names of Corne and Anderson, is used as an illustration in Bowen's *The Naval Monument*, published in 1816.

184

View of the action between the U. S. Frigate Constitution & the British Ships Levant & Cyane. Names of the three ships below the view. ☆ *Painted by Thos. Birch Eng. by J. Sartain* ☆ *Engraved for the Gentleman's Magazine, Philadelphia.* ☆ Undated.

Mezzotint. 4 13/16 in. by 8 15/16 in. In black and white.

LENT BY HENRY O. HAVEMEYER.

185

View of the action between the U. S. Frigate Constitution & the British Ships Levant & Cyane. Names of the three ships given below the view. ☆ *Aquatinted by Strickland for the Analectic Magazine and Naval Chronicle.* ☆ *Published by M. Thomas Philadelphia* ☆ Undated.

Aquatint. 3 7/8 in. by 7 3/8 in. Colored by hand. ☆ Stauffer 3054.

LENT BY IRVING S. OLDS.

To Commodore Charles Stewart. "Old Ironsides" This Song Is Cheerfully Inscribed By His Friend. The Author. Above this title is a view of the action between the *Constitution, Cyane* and *Levant.* The names of these ships and their respective commanders are stated below the view. ☆ *T. P. Otter, Del. T. Sinclair's Lith. Phil^a.* ☆ *Philadelphia Lee & Walker 188 Chestnut St.* ☆ *Song "Old Ironsides" entered according to Act of Congress A. D. 1856 by Lee & Walker.*

Lithograph. 8⅛ in. by 7⅞ in. Printed in colors.

LENT BY HENRY O. HAVEMEYER.

HORNET AND PENGUIN
MARCH 23, 1815

The last single-ship action at sea of the War of 1812 occurred on March 23, 1815, in the middle of the South Atlantic, near the Island of Tristan d'Acuna, between the American sloop-of-war *Hornet*, 20 guns, Captain James Biddle, and the British sloop-of-war, *Penguin*, 19 guns, Captain James Dickenson. News of the signing of a treaty of peace on December 24, 1814, had not then reached either of these ships.

Captain Biddle, upon sighting the *Penguin*, made sail after her. The British sloop bore up before the wind, hoisted her colors, and opened the engagement when the two ships were nearly within musket-shot distance of each other. The *Hornet* replied with a damaging broadside, and continued with a quick and well-directed fire, which was most effective. When the *Penguin* approached, as if to board, her bowsprit came in between the main and mizzen rigging of the *Hornet*. No attempt, however, was made to board. After the vessels got clear, the bowsprit and the foremast of the *Penguin* being both gone, Captain Biddle maneuvered his ship so as to be in position for a fresh broadside. The British sloop then surrendered, the action having lasted twenty-two minutes.

One was killed and eleven wounded on the *Hornet*. Only the sails and rigging of the American ship had been injured. The enemy's losses were fourteen killed, including Captain Dickenson, and twenty-eight wounded.

In view of the damaged condition of the *Penguin* and the great distance from the United States, Captain Biddle felt obliged to scuttle his prize.

The *Hornet* shortly thereafter joined the sloop-of-war *Peacock* on a cruise which took them into the Indian Ocean, where some captures of merchantmen were made.

187

To Commodore James Biddle, Esqre. This Print of H. M. Sloop of War Penguin, Captn. Dickenson; Captured Off the Island of Tristan D'Acun-ha, by the U. S. Sloop of War, Hornet, J. Biddle, Esqre. Commander on the 23rd. March 1815, after an Action of 22 Minutes. Is most respectfully dedicated, by his obedient Servant W^m. Skiddy Forces of two ships are stated at the sides. ☆ Drawn & Lith^d. by S. Walters, Liverpool, from a sketch by Captn. W^m. Skiddy ☆ Day & Haghe Lith^rs. to the Queen. ☆ Undated.

Lithograph. 10⅞ in. by 16¼ in. Colored by hand.

LENT BY BEVERLEY R. ROBINSON.

188

The Hornet and Penguin. ☆ M. Corne, p. A. Bowen, sc. ☆ Undated.

Woodcut. 3³⁄₁₆ in. by 6¾ in. In black and white.

LENT BY HENRY O. HAVEMEYER.

A similar woodcut, inscribed "The Hornet and Penguin", without the names of Corne and Bowen, is used as an illustration in Bowen's *The Naval Monument*, published in 1816.

ESCAPE OF THE HORNET
APRIL 28–30, 1815

While together in the Indian Ocean, the sloop-of-war *Hornet*, Captain James Biddle, and the sloop-of-war *Peacock*, Captain Lewis Warrington, made chase of a strange sail on the evening of April 27, 1815. The next afternoon the *Peacock* discovered that the stranger was a British 74-gun ship-of-the-line, later identified as the *Cornwallis*.

The tables were soon reversed and by night the *Cornwallis* was in hot pursuit of the *Hornet*.

The eventual escape of the *Hornet* is thus told in the official report of

Captain Biddle: " . . . as the enemy was gaining upon us, . . . I considered it necessary to lighten this ship. I therefore threw overboard 12 tons of kentledge, part of our shot, some of our heavy spars, cut away the sheet anchor and cable. . . . At daylight on the 29th, he was within gun-shot upon our lee-quarter. . . . As his shot went over us, I cut away the remaining anchor and cable, threw overboard the launch, six of our guns, more of our shot . . . at 9 A.M. he ceased his fire. At 11 A.M. the enemy was again coming up with us. I now, therefore, threw overboard all our remaining guns but one long gun, nearly all our shot, all our spare spars . . . and cleared everything off deck, as well as from below, to lighten as much as possible. . . . At sun-down the enemy was about four miles astern. . . . We saw the enemy at intervals through the squalls during the night and at daylight, on the 30th, he was about 12 miles astern, still in chase of us . . . at 11 he was entirely out of sight."

The *Hornet* put in at San Salvador on June 9, 1815, where Captain Biddle first learned of the peace between the United States and Great Britain. The *Peacock* previously had sailed on to Java.

189

H. M. S. Cornwallis of 74 Guns, in Chase of The U. S. Sloop of War, Hornet, J. Biddle, Esqre. Commander, in the Indian Ocean in 1815. To Commodore James Biddle Esqre. this Print is respectfully dedicated by his obedient Servant W^{m}. Skiddy ☆ Drawn & Lith^{d}. by S. Walters, Nelson S^{t}. Liverpool from a sketch by Capt. W^{m}. Skiddy ☆ Day & Haghe Lith^{rs}. to the Queen ☆ Undated.

Lithograph. 10⅞ in. by 16⅜ in. Colored by hand.

LENT BY BEVERLEY R. ROBINSON.

190

The Hornet's Escape From A British Seventy-Four. ☆ M. Corne, p. A. Bowen, sc. ☆ Undated.

Woodcut. 3³⁄₁₆ in. by 6¾ in. In black and white.

LENT BY HENRY O. HAVEMEYER.

A similar woodcut, inscribed "The Hornet's Escape From A British Seventy-Four", without the names of Corne and Bowen, is used as an illustration in Bowen's *The Naval Monument*, published in 1816.

PART VI

WAR WITH ALGIERS

WAR WITH ALGIERS
1815

The conclusion of the War of 1812 allowed long pent-up American shipping again to seek the seven seas. Our commerce in the Mediterranean was threatened, however, by the hostile attitude of the Dey of Algiers. Relations with that country had been tense prior to the war with Great Britain. Shortly after the ratification of the Treaty of Ghent, President Madison asked for a declaration of war against Algiers, and this action was taken by Congress on March 2, 1815.

Two squadrons, one under Commodore Stephen Decatur and the other commanded by William Bainbridge, were organized to compel the Dey to pay respect for the American flag and to enter into a satisfactory peace.

Decatur was the first to sail. After capturing the flagship of the Algerian squadron in the Mediterranean and driving an Algerian brig ashore, Decatur's fleet arrived off Algiers on June 28, 1815. President Madison's terms of peace were communicated to the Dey—a peace upon the most favored nations basis, without payment of tribute. Commodore Decatur threatened to capture the balance of the Dey's fleet unless such a peace should be made at once. Within three hours the treaty of peace was signed.

Soon thereafter the squadron under Commodore Bainbridge arrived at Algiers, and also paid visits to Tripoli and Tunis.

The appearance of these powerful squadrons in the Mediterranean had the desired effect in compelling Algiers, Tripoli and Tunis to live up to their treaties with the United States.

In September 1815, the two squadrons met at Gibraltar and sailed for home, leaving two frigates and two sloops-of-war behind to guard American shipping in the Mediterranean. It became necessary to appear before Algiers the following year with a strong American squadron under Commodore Isaac Chauncey before the Dey of Algiers finally kept his word.

191

U. S. Squadron Before The City of Algiers June 30ᵗʰ 1815. ☆ *N. Jocelin sc. N. Haven Conn:* ☆ *Undated.*

Line engraving. 3¹³⁄₁₆ in. by 6⁹⁄₁₆ in. Colored by hand. ☆ From *The Naval Temple*, Boston, 1816.

LENT BY ESTATE OF FRANCIS P. GARVAN.

192

The U. S. Squadron, under Command of Com. Decatur, At anchor off the City of Algiers, June 30ᵗʰ 1815. ☆ *Engraved by G. Munger & S. S. Jocelin.* ☆ *New Haven : Published by N. Jocelin & G. Munger. Feb. 1816.*

Aquatint. 8 in. by 13⅛ in. Colored by hand.

LENT BY RUSSELL W. THORPE.

193

United States Squadron under Com. Bainbridge returning triumphant from the Mediterranean in 1815. Names of thirteen ships below the view. ☆ *J. B. Fanning Des. G. G. Smith Sc.* ☆ *Engraved For The Naval Monument* ☆ *Entered According to Act of Congress Nov. 25, 1815, by A. Bowen Boston.*

Aquatint. 3¼ in. by 7¾ in. In black and white.

LENT BY HENRY O. HAVEMEYER.

194

Triumphant return of the American Squadron under Com. Bainbridge from the Mediterranean 1815. ☆ *M. Corne del. W. S. Leney sc.* ☆ *Printed by Samˡ. Maverick N. Y.* ☆ *Undated.*

Line engraving. 3¾ in. by 7½ in. Colored by hand.

LENT BY IRVING S. OLDS.

PART VII

PRIVATEER ACTIONS

PRIVATEER ACTIONS OF REVOLUTIONARY WAR AND WAR OF 1812

Any study of the Revolutionary War and the War of 1812 must include the privateer actions. While not now so well known to the public as historical events, they nevertheless were of considerable importance at the time and constitute a definite part of the naval history of those wars. Many of our distinguished naval commanders of this period, including Hopkins, Truxton, Barney, Barry, Rodgers, Preble, Decatur, Porter, Perry and Biddle, got their early training on board a privateer.

At that time, a privateer was a privately owned ship, armed and equipped at the expense of the owner, which was sent to sea for the purpose of preying upon enemy commerce. Her authority so to raid was a commission, usually called a letter of marque, from the Government. A portion of the money realized from the sale of prizes and their cargoes ordinarily went to the Government; the owner took a large share and the balance was divided up among officers and crew. At the beginning of the Revolution most privateers were converted merchantmen. Later on ships were constructed specially for such use.

A total of more than seven hundred American privateers sailed the seas during the seven years of our struggle for independence. They captured or destroyed about six hundred British vessels. In the War of 1812, the number of American privateers approximated five hundred and accounted for around thirteen hundred prizes. These losses were staggering blows to British commerce. Enemy privateers also extensively raided American shipping.

Space does not permit here to describe in detail any of these privateer actions. Those depicted in the few prints included in this exhibition are fairly representative of the many engagements which took place in various parts of the world.

195

A View of his Majesty's Brigg Observer, commanded by Lieu^t. John Crymes (to whom this Print is Inscribed) Engageing the American Privateer Ship Jack, John Ropes Commander, (by Night) on the 29th. of May 1782, off the Harbour of Halifax Nova Scotia. ☆ The Observer brought the Jack to Action at Nine o'Clock in the Evening, the engagement continued warm on both sides till near Midnight when the Jack struck her Colours, having her Captain & 14 Men killed with 9 wounded, the Observer 3 killed, her commander & 7 wounded. Statement of the force and armament of each ship follows. ☆ *Robt. Dodd fecit.* ☆ *London Publish'd September 1st; 1784 by Robt. Dodd N° 32 Edgeware Road.*

Aquatint. 12 in. by 17⅜ in. Colored by hand.

LENT BY H. WUNDERLICH AND O. M. TORRINGTON.

196

A View of his Majesty's Ship Mediator Commanded by the Honble James Luttrell Attacking Five Sail of the Enemy on the 12th of Decr. 1782 & throwing their Line into Confusion whereby Two of them was Captured: Viz: the Menagere the size of a Sixty Four Gun Ship Arm'd en Flute and the Alexander of 28 Guns. Statement follows of the force and armament of the British ship and of each of the three French and two American vessels involved. ☆ *Robt. Dodd Pinx^t. John Peltro Sculpsit.* ☆ *London, Publish'd Septr. 18th. 1783 by John Harris Sweetings Alley Cornhill.*

Line engraving. 11¾ in. by 16⅞ in. Colored by hand.

LENT BY H. WUNDERLICH AND O. M. TORRINGTON.

197

A View of the American Merchant Ship Planter, beating off a French National Privateer of 22 Guns July 10th. 1799. ☆ The Ships fought for two Glasses and a half, when the French Privateer sheered off to repair damages, and in one Glass return'd with his Bloody Flag hoisted, with intention to Board, but was repulsed with great Slaughter—The Action lasted five Glasses and a half, when the Privateer was completely Beat off. Statement of armament and losses of the *Planter* follows. ☆ Artist and engraver not named. ☆ *Publish'd Octr. 1st. 1800, by John Fairburn, 146, Minories, London.*

Aquatint. 9 in. by 13¾ in. Colored by hand.

LENT BY H. WUNDERLICH AND O. M. TORRINGTON.

198

The Cambrian of Boston, Willm. Marshall Master beating off a French Cutter Privateer, on 23 October 1804. ☆ Jos^h. Cartwright del. 1804 W. Barnard, Engraver. ☆ Boston, Published by C. Cave Feby. 12, 1805.

Aquatint. 12 ¾ in. by 16 ⅝ in. Colored by hand.

LENT BY H. WUNDERLICH AND O. M. TORRINGTON.

199

The Capture of the Gipsey Schooner of New York on the 30th. of April 1812, by H. M. Ships Hermes and Belle Poule. In the Middle of the Atlantic Ocean, after a Chase of three days and nights, she was bound from New York to Bordeaux with a Cargo Value 50,000 L. The Schooner was a most superb Vessel of 300 Tons burthen carried Ten 18^lb Carronades and one long 18 pound swivel between her main & foremast with a complement of 80 Men & 2 Ferocious Dogs. She had twice surrender'd to the Hermes previous to falling in with the Belle Poule & endeavoured to effect her escape each time by hauling off on a different tack, while the ship was in the act of taking in sail & rounding to. The Crew of the American made a desperate effort to regain possession of their Vessel after being boarded by the boats of the Hermes by 20 Armed Men and the Two Dogs suddenly assailing them, which after a severe struggle were overpowered. ☆ Painted by W. J. Huggins, Marine Painter to His Majesty for Charles Augustus Manning, Esqre. Portland Castle, Dorsetshire, from a Design by Captn. Philip Browne, R. N. Commander of H. M. S. Hermes. Engraved by C. Rosenberg. ☆ Undated.

Aquatint. 10 ½ in. by 17 ⅛ in. Colored by hand.

LENT BY BEVERLEY R. ROBINSON.

200

To Francis Freeling Esqr. Secretary to the General Post Office This Plate representing the situation of H. M. Packet Hinchinbrook at the close of an Engagement with the American Privateer, Grand Turk of Salem, on the 1 of May 1814. The action commenced at 5 hrs: 20 min P. M. and continued until 7 hrs 30 min within pistol shot, during which the Enemy twice laid the Packet aboard but was beaten off; after the failure of the second attempt, the Hinchinbrook obtained a raking position, disabled and obliged the Privateer to sheer off Is very respectfully dedicated by his most obed^t. humble Servt. Willm. James Comm^n Statement of the force and armament of each ship follows. ☆ Drawn by W. I. Pocock. Engraved by

ENGAGEMENT BETWEEN THE AMERICAN PRIVATEER GRAND TURK AND THE
BRITISH POST-OFFICE PACKET HINCHINBROOK, MAY 1, 1814

Engraved by John Baily after a drawing by W. I. Pocock

(See No. 200)

Baily 48 Tufton Str. Westminster. ☆ *Pub. Feb. 1, 1819 by Messrs. Colnaghi & Cº.*
23 Cockspur Str. for the Proprietor.   *Illustrated*

Aquatint. 11 15/16 in. by 17 3/4 in. Colored by hand.

LENT BY BEVERLEY R. ROBINSON.

201

*Battle between the Schooner Atlas and two British Ships, on the 5th. of August
1812.* ☆ *A. Weingartner's Lithy. N. Y.* ☆ Undated.

Lithograph. 3 7/16 in. by 6 1/8 in. In sepia.

202

*Battle between the Schooner Rossie, and the Ship Princess Amelia, on the 16th. of
Sept. 1812.* ☆ *A. Weingartner's Lithy. N. Y.* ☆ Undated.

Lithograph. 3 7/16 in. by 6 3/16 in. In sepia.

203

*Battle between the Schooner Saratoga, and the Brig Rachel, on the 15th. of Dec.
1812.* ☆ *A. Weingartner's Lithy. N. Y.* ☆ Undated.

Lithograph. 3 7/16 in. by 6 3/16 in. In sepia.

204

*Battle between the Schooner Dolphin, the British Ship Hebe and a Brig, off Cape
St. Vincent, on the 25th. of Jan. 1813.* ☆ *A. Weingartner's Lithy. N. Y.* ☆ Undated.

Lithograph. 3 7/16 in. by 6 3/16 in. In sepia.

205

*Battle between the Schooner Decatur and the Schooner Dominica, on the 5th. of
August 1813.* ☆ *A. Weingartner's Lithy. N. Y.* ☆ Undated.

Lithograph. 3 1/2 in. by 6 3/16 in. In sepia.

206

*Battle between the Brig Chasseur, and the Schooner St. Lawrence, off Havanna on
the 26th. of Feb. 1815.* ☆ *A. Weingartner's Lithy. N. Y.* ☆ Undated.

Lithograph. 3 3/8 in. by 6 3/16 in. In sepia.

ABOVE DESCRIBED SIX LITHOGRAPHS LENT BY ROBERT FRIDENBERG.

ADAM WEINGARTNER carried on a lithographic business at New York under
his own name during the years 1854 to 1863. Prior to that time, he had been a
partner in the firm of Nagel & Weingartner. In addition to marine prints, Weingartner issued some interesting New York views.

PART VIII

MISCELLANEOUS PRINTS AND OTHER ITEMS

207

Capt[n]. James Mugford, of the Schr. Franklin Continental Cruiser 1776. ☆ Oval portrait, with a view of the capture of the British Transport Ship *Hope* forming the background. ☆ This print contains the following description of that capture: "One of the heroic men with Thomas Russell, 1st Lieut. and 19 Officers and men from Marblehead who captured the armed British Transport Ship *Hope* Ladened with Powder, implements of War and Pioneer Tools, destined for and in sight of the British Admiralty Fleet then in Nantasket Roads Nov[r]. 1775. The scarcity of Powder was severely felt by the Continental Congress the procuring of it attracted their particular and constant attention, every encouragement had been held by them to the inhabitants of the Country, to engage in the manufacture thereof, no opportunity was neglected in importing, or seizing it from the Enemy.—March 1776 Gen[l]. Washington entered Boston in triumph, the British evacuated and embarked, and lay in Nantasket Roads, waiting the arrival of their Powder Ship—The enterprising and heroic Mugford, with Officers and men captured said Ship and transfered her with Cargo to the United States Commissary Gen[l]. and Quarter Master, by the Continental Agent, Col. Jonathan Glover. This was One of the most valuable prizes during the Revolution, the principal and interest to 1854, Amounts to 1,349,343 15/100 Dollars! this and similar events produced the general voice—"We will be free." Congress deliberately and solemnly decided to declare it to the world; and the Declaration of Independence was agreed to in Congress on the 4th of July 1776. Who can estimate the real value of that capture?" ☆ *L. H. Bradford & Co's Lith.* ☆ Undated.

Lithograph. 9 in. by 16 in. Colored by hand.

LENT BY HENRY O. HAVEMEYER.

208

Campagne du Vice-Amiral Cte. d'Estaing en Amérique, commandant une Escadre de 12 Vaisseaux et 4 frégattes, sortie de Toulon le 13 avril 1778. N°. V This title at the top of the view. ☆ *L'escadre Forcant l'entrée de la baye de Rhode–Island sous le feu des batteries.* This inscription is below the view, followed by a descriptive text, with lettered references keyed to similar letters on the drawing.

Wash sepia drawing by Pierre Ozanne. 9⅜ in. by 16 in.

Twenty-two drawings of a series by Pierre Ozanne are in the Library of Congress at Washington. See Stokes and Haskell, page 55.

209

Preparation for War to defend Commerce. The Swedish Church Southwark with the building of the Frigate Philadelphia. ☆ *Drawn Engraved & Published by W. Birch and Son.* ☆ *Sold by R. Campbell & Cº. Nº. 30 Chesnut Street. Philadª. 1800.*

Line engraving. 9⅛ in. by 11⅞ in. Colored by hand. ☆ Stauffer 170.

210

Episode de La Guerre de L'Indépendence Dessiné et Lith. par Ferd. Perrot Lith. Coulon r. richer, 7. Paris, chez Victor Delarue, Editeur, Place du Louvre, 10. ☆ Undated. View shown in this print is not identified.

Lithograph. 11⅜ in. by 16¾ in. Colored by hand.

211

Combat Naval Episode de la Guerre des Etats-Unis contre L'Angleterre. Etudes de Marines par Fᵈ. Perrot. Nº. 30. ☆ *Ferdᵈ. Perrot Im. de Lemercier, Benard et Cⁱᵉ à Paris, chez Victor Delarue. éditeur, Place du Louvre, 10.*

Lithograph. 11⅝ in. by 16¾ in. Colored by hand. ☆ This is probably a view of the action between the *Bon Homme Richard* and the *Serapis.*

Another identical lithograph, owned by Henry O. Havemeyer, is inscribed: "Lith Rigo Fʳˢ et Cⁱᵉ rue Richer 7."

212

Sprigs of Laurel. ☆ Large view of *Perry's Victory* at top, below which are eight rectangular views of naval engagements or incidents of the War of 1812, inscribed: *Constitution & Guerriere United States & Macedonian Hornet Blockading Bonne*

Citoyenne Enterprise and Boxer Wasp & Frolic Constitution and Java Sinking of the Peacock, and *Peacock & L'Epervier*. ☆ *Drawn & Engraved by W. Strickland* ☆ *Philadelphia. Pub: by John Kneass 125 Market St Price three Dols.* ☆ Undated.

Aquatint. 19⅞ in. by 14½ in. Colored by hand. ☆ Fielding 1522.

LENT BY IRVING S. OLDS.

213

Splendid Victories gained by the United States Frigates over the British since the commencement of the present War. ☆ Three vertical oval panels containing views of the actions between the *Constitution* and *Guerrière*, *United States* and *Macedonian*, and *Frolic* and *Wasp*, with the names *Decatur, Hull* and *Jones* above the panels. *Bainbridge* also appears above the central panel. ☆ Statement at bottom of print giving the dates and places of the actions, the vessels engaged and the names of their commanders. ☆ *New Haven March 20th. 1813 Published by A. Doolittle Engraver.*

Line engraving. 8⅞ in. by 14½ in. Tinted by hand. ☆ Fielding 360.

LENT BY HENRY GRAVES, JR.

214

U. S. Frigate Constitution, of 44 Guns. ☆ *Drawn by Wm. Lynn.* ☆ *A. Bowen Sc.* ☆ *Boston, Publ. by Wm. Lynn.* ☆ Undated.

Line engraving. 16⅛ in. by 21⅜ in. Partially colored by hand. ☆ Stauffer 233.

Illustrated on cover

LENT BY PEABODY MUSEUM, SALEM, MASS.

215

Frigate United States. ☆ *T. Clarke Sculpt Philada.* ☆ Undated. ☆ *For the American Universal Magazine..*

Line engraving. 3⁵⁄₁₆ in. by 5¹⁄₁₆ in. In black and white.

LENT BY ROBERT FRIDENBERG.

216

An Improved Map of the United States by Shelton & Kensett.

In the space indicating the Atlantic Ocean are nine small engraved vignettes of the naval engagements between the *Chesapeak and Shannon; Constitution and Guerriere; Essex and Allert; Memorable Action fought by Com Perry; Wasp and*

Frolick; Constitution and Java; Hornet and Peacock; Argus and Pelican; and *United States and Macedonian.* In the side and lower margins are given the mileage between various points, the population of each state and the territorial governments, etc.

Engraved by A. Doolittle New Haven. Copy right secured, & entered according to Act of Congress Nov^r*. 8*th*. 1813. Published by Shelton & Kensett Cheshire Connec*^{t} *Nov*^{r} *8*th *1813*

Line engraving. 17⅞ in. by 19¼ in. In black and white.

There is a similar map of the United States by Shelton & Kensett, containing seven small engraved vignettes of naval engagements, with the following engraving and publication data: "Engraved by A. Doolittle New Haven and T. Kensett Cheshire. Copy right secured, & entered according to Act of Congress July 6th. 1813."

THOMAS KENSETT (1786–1829) was born in England, but early in life came to Connecticut. About 1806 he published a map of New Haven. In 1812, he was a member of the engraving and print publishing firm of Shelton & Kensett of Cheshire, Conn. Kensett's name as engraver appears upon a map of Upper and Lower Canada, published in November 1812.

217

Oval portraits of *Perry, Hull* and *Decatur,* with views below of actions between *Constitution & Guerriere Aug 19*th*. 1812; Perry's Victory. Sept. 10*th*. 1813;* and *United States & Macedonian Oct 25*th*. 1812.* In three separate sheets, framed together. ☆ Artists and engravers not named. ☆ Undated.

Line & stipple engravings. 7½ in. by 3⅞ in. (two side sheets) 9 in. by 7 in. (centre sheet). Colored by hand.

218

Engraving containing twelve small medallion portraits of *James Lawrence, Esq*^{r}*. Late of the United States Navy; Jacob Jones, Esq*^{r}*. of the United States Navy; Robert Fulton Esq*^{r}*.; Major Gen*^{l}*. Andrew Jackson; Isaac Hull Esq*^{r}*. of the United States Navy; General Pike. Late of the United States Army; James Monroe President of the United States; William Bainbridge Esq*^{r}*. of the United States Navy; Oliver H. Perry Esq. of the United States Navy; Jonathan Russell Esq*^{r}*. Minister*

Plenipotentiary of the U. S.; Major Genl. Brown, U. S. Army; and Major Genl. Winfield Scott of the United States Army, with two small circular views of naval engagements below, entitled: *The U. S. Frigate Constitution Isaac Hull Esqr. Commander Capturing His B. M's Frigate Guerriere August 19th. 1812*, and *The U. S. Frigate United States Stephen Decatur Esqr. Commander Capturing His B. M's Frigate Macedonian October 25th. 1812*. Artist, engraver and publisher not named. ☆ Undated. Presumably issued during the Presidency of James Monroe. Line engraving. 15¼ in. by 16¼ in., exclusive of small circular views. In black and white.

LENT BY IRVING S. OLDS.

219

Hatred of Sin. School sheet containing five verses of poetry in pen and ink beneath the title, signed "Josiah Shaw, June 20th 1820." ☆ *British Valour. Capture of the U. S. frigate President Commodore Decatur by the Endymion Frigate Captain Hope. after an anxious chase of eighteen hours and a half, Jany. 15, 1815*. Statement of armament and crew of each ship follows. ☆ Two small engravings at each side of the poem, inscribed: *The Gallant Captain Hope giving orders to his crew. Commodore Decatur ordering the Anchors to be thrown overboard. Crippled State of the Enemy's Ship at the close of the Action. Commodore Decatur giving up his sword to Captain Hope*. ☆ *Published by J. Fairburn, Junr. Fountain Court, Minories, sold also by Champante & Whitrow Jewry Street*. ☆ Artist and engraver not named. ☆ Undated.

Line engraving. 16½ in. by 13 in. In black and white.

LENT BY H. WUNDERLICH AND O. M. TORRINGTON.

220

We Have Met The Enemy And They Are Ours. (on pennant at top) ☆ *Here, Freemen, view that diplomatic Power*, ☆ *Which gave back Peace to Freedom's happy Bower*, ☆ *T'was thus you urg'd an injur'd Nation's Right*, ☆ *And prov'd the Conquerors in the dreadful Fight*, ☆ *But tis enough—America forbear!* ☆ *Cherish the Laurels which your Temples wear;* ☆ *Furl Mars' red Banner, bid the Trumpet cease*, ☆ *And long Repose within the Bower of Peace*. ☆ Two central rectangular panels, inscribed: *Perry's Victory on Lake Erie Sept 10 1813 Macdonough's Victory on Lake Champlain. Sept. 11 1814*. Four smaller rectangular panels at each side, inscribed: *Constitution & Guerriere Aug 19 1812 Wasp and Frolic Oct 18 1812 Constitution & Java Dec 29 1812 Enterprise & Boxer Sept 4 1813 United States & Macedonian Oct 25 1812 Essex & Alert Aug 13 1812 Hornet & Pea-*

cock Feb 24 1813 Epervier & Peacock April 29 1814 ☆ Artist and engraver not named. ☆ Undated. Presumably published shortly after Treaty of Ghent, signed on December 24, 1814.

Line engraving. 14⅝ in. by 19½ in. In black and white.

221

Launch of the Steam Frigate Fulton the First, At New York, 29ᵗʰ. Octʳ. 1814. 150 feet long and 50 feet wide, will mount 28 long 32 pounders, and 2 50 pounders (Columbiards) ☆ *Drawn by J. J. Barralet, from a Sketch by—Morgan, taken on the spot. B. Tanner direxᵗ.* ☆ *Philadelphia, Published 27ᵗʰ March 1815 by B. Tanner, Nᵒ. 74 South 8ᵗʰ Sᵗ.* ☆ First state.

Line engraving. 9⅞ in. by 14¾ in. In black and white.

See I. N. Phelps Stokes' *Iconography of Manhattan Island*, pp. 556–57.

A later state of this print is listed in Stauffer as No. 3131. It bears a publication line reading: "Published by Cammeyer & Acock, Nᵒ. 10 Library Street Philadᵃ 1819."

In 1814, during the War of 1812, the citizens of New York because of the defenseless state of New York Harbor offered to advance the funds required to build a new type of frigate, designed by Robert Fulton, which was to be operated by steam and used as a floating battery for the defense of the adjacent coastal waters. The boat was of a catamaran type, the boiler being in one hull and the machinery in the other. A large paddlewheel operated in a sluice between the two hulls. On October 29, 1814, the *Fulton the First* was launched at New York. The War of 1812 ended, however, before the completion of the new frigate. She eventually became a receiving ship at the Brooklyn Navy Yard. This ship was the first ironclad steam vessel ever built. *The Fulton the First* was destroyed by an explosion of her powder magazine on June 4, 1829.

222

Naval Heroes of the United States ☆ The print has eight oval portraits of *Perry, Decatur, Macdonough, Preble, Barney, Barry, Dale,* and *Bainbridge. Kelloggs & Thayer, 144 Fulton Street, New York* ☆ *Entered according to act of Congress, on the year 1846, by Kelloggs & Thayer, in the clerk's office, in the district court for the southern district of N. Y.*

Lithograph. 13¹⁄₁₆ in. by 9⁹⁄₁₆ in. Colored by hand.

223

In memory of Commodore Oliver H. Perry, who captured the British Squadron on Lake Erie, Septr. 10th. 1813. ☆ The American Eagle lamenting the death of Perry— His family at the monument—Religion administering Consolation Liberty within the Temple of Fame laying his sword upon the altar—The Frigate in which he sailed returning with colours at half mast. ☆ On base of monument: *Sacred to the Memory of Commodore Oliver Hazard Perry, of the United States Navy; Who departed this life August 23^d. 1819, Aged 34 Years.* Further inscription on upper part of monument. Small portrait of Com. Oliver H. Perry at bottom. ☆ *Drawn by E. C. Brenton. Engraved by W. H. Bassett & A. Willard. ☆ Entered according to act of Congress by Elizabeth C. Brenton, Feb 5th 1———*

Line engraving. 16¾ in. by 23⅛ in. Colored by hand. ☆ Stauffer 3387.

LENT BY IRVING S. OLDS.

224

U. S. Naval Carpenter & Machine Shop, Port Royal, S. C. ☆ A. T. Florence del^t. Ja^s. M^c. Guigan Lith. Philad^a.

Lithograph. 8⅜ in. by 13⅜ in. Colored by hand. ☆ Undated.

LENT BY CARL W. DREPPERD.

225

Battle of Plattsburgh, and Victory on Lake Champlain, In Which 14,000 British mymidons were defeated and put to flight by 5,000 Yankees and Green-mountain Boys on the memorable Eleventh of Sept. 1814. Contemporaneous broadside containing 34 small panels of wood engravings, including *M'Donough's Ship, Capt. Downie, Gen Macomb,* and *Gov. Prevost.* ☆ Artist and engraver not named. ☆ Undated.

Woodcuts. 17½ in. by 23 in. In black and white.

LENT BY HALL PARK McCULLOUGH.

226

Four contemporaneous broadsides, entitled *Hull's Victory* (Sold by Nathaniel Coverly Jun. Corner Theatre-Alley), *Huzza for the Constitution, Captain Hull's Victory,* and *Bainbridge's Victory.*

227

Receipt signed by The Chevalier Paul Jones, dated Philadelphia 26th June 1781, covering the payment of £1400, 5 sh. as his pay in the Navy from December 7, 1775 to May 10, 1776 as Senior First Lieutenant and from May 10, 1776 to June 26, 1781 as Captain.

228

Two receipts, each dated August 3, 1798, for materials, etc. used in the construction of the U. S. Frigate *Constitution*.

229

A ship's lantern of the kind used on board the United States 44-gun frigates, such as the *Constitution, Constellation* and *United States*, is included in this exhibition.

THE ABOVE FOUR ITEMS ARE LENT BY HALL PARK McCULLOUGH.

230

Original commission to James Lawrence as Master Commandant in the United States Navy, signed by President James Madison. Dated November 3, 1810.

LENT BY THE NEW YORK HISTORICAL SOCIETY FROM THE JAMES LAWRENCE COLLECTION FORMED BY DR. EUGENE H. POOL.

230a

Small wooden snuff-box with engraved views in colors of the engagement between the *United States* and *Macedonian* and the engagement between the *Constitution* and *Guerriere*.

LENT BY HENRY O. HAVEMEYER.

PART IX

AMERICAN NAVAL COMMANDERS

WILLIAM HENRY ALLEN

William Henry Allen was born at Providence, R. I., on October 21, 1784, a son of General William Allen of Revolutionary War distinction. He was appointed a Midshipman in the United States Navy on April 28, 1800, and assigned to the frigate *George Washington* under Captain William Bainbridge. After several years in the Mediterranean during the War with Tripoli, Allen was ordered as a junior lieutenant to the frigate *Chesapeake* and was on board that vessel at the time of the unfortunate incident with the British ship *Leopard*. Allen signed a petition protesting against the action of his commanding officer in not preparing the *Chesapeake* for action.

Allen was First Lieutenant on the frigate *United States* when she captured the British frigate *Macedonian*. Receiving command of the sloop-of-war *Argus*, Allen took Mr. Crawford, the new Minister to France, to his destination. Shortly thereafter, the *Argus* met the British brig *Pelican* on August 14, 1813, and after a fierce action was forced to surrender. Allen received a mortal wound during the fight and died in England a few days later.

231

W^m. Henry Allen Esq. late of the United States Navy ☆ Edwin sc.

Stipple engraving. Vignette. 3^{13}⁄₁₆ in. by 3¼ in. ☆ Stauffer 700.

WILLIAM BAINBRIDGE

William Bainbridge was born at Princeton, N. J., on May 7, 1774. He went to sea at the age of fifteen. His first experience in a naval action was while in command of the *Hope*, a merchantman armed with four guns, which captured a larger British privateer. Bainbridge joined Commodore Truxton's squadron in 1798, being in command of the *Norfolk*. In 1800, he was made a Captain in the United States Navy, when only 25 years of age. In the same year he was required to carry tribute to the Dey of Algiers.

In 1803, Bainbridge had command of the frigate *Philadelphia* which had the misfortune to run aground near Tripoli, resulting in her capture. Bainbridge was a prisoner at Tripoli for many months. In 1812, he was given command of the frigate *Constitution* and while cruising off Brazil captured the British frigate *Java* in a brilliantly fought engagement. Bainbridge commanded a squadron in the War with Algiers in 1815. He died at Philadelphia on July 27, 1833.

232

W. Bainbridge Esqr. U. S. N. ☆ Stuart Pinxt. Edwin Sculpt. ☆ Vignette below of the action between the *Constitution* and *Java*, inscribed: *Kearney delt. et sculpt.*

Stipple engraving. Rectangular. 4¹¹⁄₁₆ in. by 3¹¹⁄₁₆ in. ☆ Stauffer 708. ☆ Stauffer lists this engraving as having a publication line reading: "Published by M. Thomas Philᵃ."

DAVID EDWIN (1776–1841) was born in Bath, England. He arrived in Philadelphia at the age of twenty-one. Apprenticed to a Dutch engraver in London, Edwin later went with his master to Holland and from there came to America. In Philadelphia, Edwin was first employed by the book publisher, T. B. Freeman, and then by Edward Savage. Edwin's marked ability as an engraver of portraits in stipple soon was recognized, and he became the most popular and prolific engraver of portraits in the United States. Edwin engraved numerous portraits of the prominent naval commanders of the War of 1812.

233

Commodore Bainbridge Captur'd and destroyed the Java. Ribbon beneath the portrait, inscribed: *Avast! Boys She's Struck. ☆ G. Delleker Sc. ☆ Published by J. Kneass 125 Market St. Philᵃ.*

Line engraving. Vignette with laurel branches and ribbon below. 4½ in. by 3½ in. Colored by hand. ☆ Stauffer 477.

GEORGE DELLEKER is best known for his engraved portraits of the naval commanders of the War of 1812. His name appears as an engraver in the Philadelphia directories from 1817 through 1824. Probably Delleker was carrying on an engraving business in Philadelphia prior to 1817. Later Delleker and G. H. Young conducted a general engraving business in Philadelphia under the name of Delleker & Young.

JOSHUA BARNEY

Joshua Barney was born in Baltimore on July 6, 1759. At the age of twelve he went to sea. When only fifteen, he assumed command of a merchant ship upon the sudden death of her master and brought the vessel safely to port. In 1775, Barney became Master's Mate of the *Hornet*, and the following year a Lieutenant. In 1782, after having been twice made prisoner by the British, Barney became Commander of the *Hyder-Ally*, a converted merchantman, with which he achieved a signal victory in capturing the *General Monk*, a more heavily armed British vessel. From 1796 to 1802 he served as a Captain in the French Navy against the British.

Barney rejoined the American Navy in 1805. In 1814, he was in command of a flotilla in the Potomac in the defence of Washington. At the approach of a much superior British force, he took his guns and men ashore, where a heroic but unsuccessful stand was made against the enemy. Barney was wounded in this encounter. He died on December 1, 1818, at Pittsburgh, Pa.

234

Commodore Barney. Wood, Pinxᵗ. Childs & Gimber, Scᵗ.

Stipple engraving. Oval vignette. 5 in. by 4 in. ☆ Stauffer 340.

CEPHAS G. CHILDS (1793–1871), a native of Pennsylvania, made his reputation as an engraver in Philadelphia, where he was listed in the city directory for nearly thirty years as an "historical and landscape engraver." Early in his career, he was a member of the firm of Childs & Carpenter, and later of the firm of Childs & Gimber. Childs engraved many of the plates for his *Views of Philadelphia* and also produced some creditable portraits. In 1831, Childs associated himself with the artist, Henry Inman. The firm of Childs & Inman continued for four years, during period P. S. Duval was brought from Europe to head their lithographic department. Albert Newsam, a deaf and dumb lithographer, executed some of the best work on stone for the firm and became one of the country's foremost lithographic artists. About 1845 Childs abandoned engraving and became a newspaper editor at Philadelphia.

JAMES BARRON

James Barron was born in 1769, a son of a naval commander of the same name. He distinguished himself as a junior officer on the frigate *United States*, and later was given command of the frigate *Essex*, and then of the frigate *President*.

He was engaged in the operations in the Mediterranean against the Barbary States until 1805, for a time being in command of the Mediterranean squadron.

As commander of the frigate *Chesapeake* in 1807 Barron was hailed a few miles off the American coast by the British frigate *Leopard* and his ship was searched for British deserters, a few sailors being forcibly taken away from the *Chesapeake*. In a subsequent court martial in 1808, Barron was suspended from the service for five years without pay "for neglecting, on the probability of an engagement, to clear his ship for action." He never again resumed active service in the Navy. Barron killed Commodore Stephen Decatur in a duel on March 22, 1820. His own death occurred on April 21, 1851.

235

Commodore James Barron, of The U. S. Navy. ☆ *Engraved by J. W. Steel, from the Original Painting by Neagle.*

Line engraving. Rectangular. 5⅛ in. by 4³⁄₁₆ in. ☆ Stauffer 3000.

JAMES W. STEEL (1799–1879) was born in Philadelphia. He became a pupil of the Philadelphia engravers, Benjamin Tanner and George Murray. For a time he did engraving work for Tanner, Vallance, Kearney & Co., in his native city. Later he established his own reputation as a line engraver, producing portrait, landscapes, and annual plates. In the latter part of his life he devoted his talents to bank-note engraving.

JOHN BARRY

John Barry was born in Ireland in 1745. He came to Philadelphia in 1760. Taking up the sea for a profession, he became a merchant ship captain. At the outbreak of the Revolution, Barry was in command of the *Lexington*, with which he later captured the *Edward*. He then stood seventh on the list of captains. Barry participated in various actions in the Delaware during 1777–78. In 1781, he commanded the *Alliance*. Barry took an active part in the Quasi-War with France, being in command of all our naval forces in the West Indies. He died on September 13, 1803.

John Barry. U.S.N. Facsimile signature below. *Engraved by J. B. Longacre from a painting by G. Stuart.*

Line engraving. Rectangular. 4½ in. by 3⅝ in. ☆ Stauffer 1928.

JAMES B. LONGACRE (1794–1869) was born in Delaware County, Pa. He was taught to engrave in Philadelphia by George Murray. His earliest notable plate was a portrait of Andrew Jackson after the painting by Thomas Sully. This engraving was published in 1820. Many of his subsequent portraits were after his own drawings from life. He was one of the originators of the *American Portrait Gallery*, an ambitious undertaking consisting of a series of biographical sketches, illustrated by portraits, of American statesmen, military and naval heroes. Longacre engraved a number of the portraits for this work and in other instances drew the original portraits for others to engrave. In 1844 Longacre was appointed engraver to the U. S. Mint, a position which he held until his death.

237

Commodore John Barry ☆ *Stuart pinx. Edwin sc.*

Stipple engraving. Oval. 3¾ in. by 3⅛ in. ☆ Stauffer 711.

JAMES BIDDLE

James Biddle was born in Philadelphia on February 18, 1783. After studying at the University of Pennsylvania, he became a Midshipman in the Navy in 1800. He was an officer on the frigate *Philadelphia* and was captured when that vessel was taken over by the Tripolitans, following her going ashore off Tripoli. He remained a prisoner in Tripoli for 19 months.

Biddle obtained his first independent command when he took charge of the sloop *Siren* in 1810. He was an officer on the *Wasp* when the latter captured the British brig *Frolic*. Shortly after this engagement, both the *Wasp* and *Frolic* were captured by the British ship-of-the-line *Poictiers*. Biddle was paroled at Bermuda in 1813, and again engaged in active service during the remainder of the War of 1812. He was in command of the sloop-of-war *Hornet* when she captured the British sloop-of-war *Penguin* near the Island of Tristan d'Acuna in the South Atlantic on March 23, 1815. Biddle died in Philadelphia on October 1, 1848.

238

James Biddle Esqr. Of the United States Navy. ☆ *Wood, del. Gimbrede, Sculp^t.* ☆ *Engraved for the Analectic Magazine.* ☆ *Published by M. Thomas.*

Stipple engraving. Rectangular. 3¹⁵⁄₁₆ in. by 3⁵⁄₁₆ in. ☆ Stauffer 1037.

239

James Biddle Esq. of the United States Navy. ☆ *J. Wood pinx. Gimbrede sc.*

Stipple engraving. Rectangular. 3⅞ in. by 3¼ in. ☆ Stauffer 1038. Differs from the preceding engraving.

NICHOLAS BIDDLE

Nicholas Biddle was born in Philadelphia on September 10, 1750. After some years in the merchant ship service, he joined the British Navy in 1772. The following year he abandoned his naval career and became a member of a polar expedition, in which he found himself in the company of Horatio Nelson.

Biddle offered his services to the Continental Congress at the beginning of the Revolution. He was given a commission and conducted a number of successful actions against vessels of the British Navy and of the merchant marine. In 1778, while commanding the *Randolph* he encountered off Charleston the British ship-of-the-line *Yarmouth*, carrying 64 guns. The *Randolph* was blown up in this engagement, and Biddle perished at the age of 27, together with the great majority of his officers and crew.

Nicholas Biddle had a son of the same name, who became President of the Bank of the United States in 1823.

240

Capt. Nicholas Biddle. ☆ *D. Edwin sc.*

Stipple engraving. Rectangular. 4¼ in. by 3¼ in. ☆ Stauffer 714.

JOHNSTON BLAKELEY

Johnston Blakeley was born in Ireland in October, 1781, and at the age of two was brought by his father to Wilmington, N. C. In 1800 Blakeley became a Midshipman in the Navy and took part in the operations of the American squadron before Tripoli.

In 1813, Blakeley was given command of the sloop-of-war *Wasp*. After making a number of captures of merchantmen in the vicinity of the English Channel, the *Wasp* engaged and captured the British brig *Reindeer* on June 28, 1814. A few months later the *Wasp*, still under the command of Blakeley, successfully engaged the British brig *Avon*, although later compelled to abandon her prize. Toward the end of 1814, the *Wasp* disappeared while cruising in the South Atlantic and nothing more was ever heard of Blakeley or his vessel and its crew.

241

Johnston Blakely E^sq of the United States Navy ☆ *Gimbrede Sculp^t*
Stipple engraving. Rectangular. 3⅜ in. by 2⁹⁄₁₆ in. ☆ Second state, without the publication line reading: "Engraved for the Analectic Magazine and Naval Chronicle. Published by M. Thomas." ☆ Stauffer 1039.

ISAAC CHAUNCEY

Isaac Chauncey was born at Black Rock, Conn., on February 20, 1772. At the age of nineteen he was given command of the ship *Jenny* belonging to the Schermerhorns of New York. During one of his voyages between Charleston and New York all the crew and officers except himself were stricken with yellow fever, and he brought the vessel into port "single-handed". He became a Lieutenant in the Navy in 1798. Chauncey had command of several vessels during the War with Tripoli, and for his services was awarded a sword by Congress.

In August of 1812, Chauncey was made commander of the naval forces on Lakes Ontario and Erie. He was charged with the mission of constructing an adequate naval force on each of these important lakes. The fleet assembled on Lake Erie achieved a notable success in the Battle of Lake Erie under the immediate command of Commodore O. H. Perry. No outstanding victory was ever achieved on Lake Ontario. Accordingly, it has been said of Chauncey that he was excessively cautious, and inactive at critical moments. Chauncey died at Washington, D. C., on February 27, 1840.

242

Hero of Lake Ontario—Commodore Chauncey of Lake Ontario pub. by P. Price Jʳ. Philadᵃ.

Line engraving. Vignette. 4½ in. by 4⅛ in., with hand colored laurel wreath and ribbon below the portrait.

243

Isaac Chauncey Esqʳ. of the United States Navy. ☆ *J. Wood pinxt. D. Edwin sc.* ☆ *Engraved for the Analectic Magazine* ☆ *Published by M. Thomas.*

Stipple engraving. Rectangular. 3¾ in. by 3³⁄₁₆ in. ☆ Stauffer 727. Another state omits the names of the magazine and publisher.

244

Isaac Chauncey Esqʳ. of the United States Navy ☆ Artist and engraver not named.

Stipple engraving. Circular. 3³⁄₁₆ in. in diameter.

GUSTAVUS CONYNGHAM

Gustavus Conyngham was born in County Donegal, Ireland, about 1744. He came to Philadelphia in 1763, subsequently going to sea as an apprentice. In 1776, he became stranded in Europe when his merchant ship was seized by the British.

While in Paris, he received a commission in the Continental Navy on March 1, 1777, from the American Commissioners in France. His first command, the *Surprise*, a lugger, took several valuable prizes. Later he became captain of the cutter *Revenge* and with her so demoralized British shipping that he became known in legend as "Le terreur des Anglais." These vessels operated from Dunkirk, France, and Ferrol, Spain.

Conyngham arrived in Philadelphia on February 21, 1779, having taken sixty prizes in eighteen months. He was captured on April 27, 1779, and imprisoned in England. Conyngham escaped to Holland in November 1779, joined Paul Jones and was again captured. Later he was exchanged. He died in Philadelphia on November 27, 1819.

245

Cap^n. Cuningham. ☆ Engraved from the Original Sketch which was taken by an Artist of Eminence, and stuck up in the English Coffee House at DunKirk. And was greatly admired there as a good characterestic Likeness.

Line engraving. 5½ in. by 4 in.

246

Augustatus Kuningam Fameux Marin Commodore au Service des Etats unis de l'Amerique et le Terreur des Anglais.

Line engraving. 9⁹⁄₁₆ in. by 7¹³⁄₁₆ in.

RICHARD DALE

Richard Dale was born in Virginia on November 6, 1756. He went to sea at the age of twelve, served his apprenticeship and had risen to be Chief Mate by 1775. In 1776 he became a Lieutenant, serving on one of the small boats operating off Virginia. While so engaged, he was captured. Later Dale sailed for France in the *Lexington* as Master's Mate. Again he was captured.

Dale escaped from imprisonment in England and joined John Paul Jones, who made him second in command of the *Bon Homme Richard*. Dale was wounded in the famous action with the *Serapis*. He continued to serve with Jones through 1779–80. From 1783 to 1794 he was in the merchant marine service.

In 1794 Dale became a Captain in our Navy. He served off and on until 1802 in the Far East and the Mediterranean. Thereafter he lived in Philadelphia as a private citizen until his death on February 26, 1826.

247

Richard Dale Esq. late of the United States Navy. ☆ *Wood pinxᵗ. Edwin sc.*
Stipple engraving. Oval. 3¹³⁄₁₆ in. by 3⅛ in. ☆ Stauffer 743.

STEPHEN DECATUR

Stephen Decatur was born in Maryland on January 5, 1779. He was commissioned a Midshipman on April 30, 1798, and sailed on board the frigate *United States* under Commodore Barry. He became a Lieutenant and was assigned to the *Essex*, forming a part of Commodore Dale's squadron in the Mediterranean before Tripoli. In 1803, Decatur commanded the *Enterprise*, in which he captured the ketch *Intrepid*. With a volunteer crew on board the *Intrepid*, Decatur accomplished without loss of life the burning of the frigate *Philadelphia*, which had been captured by the Tripolitans. Lord Nelson called this "the most bold and daring act of the age."

At the outbreak of the War of 1812, Decatur was given command of the frigate *United States*, with which he captured the British frigate *Macedonian* on October 25, 1812. Decatur was captain of the frigate *President*, when, after successfully engaging the British frigate *Endymion*, she was obliged to strike her colors to a British squadron on January 16, 1815. He died on March 22, 1820, following a duel with Commodore James Barron.

248

Commodore Stephen Decatur. Small vignette below of engagement between *United States* and *Macedonian.* ☆ *Wᵐ. Birch pinxit. Freeman Excudit. D. Edwin sculp.*

Stipple engraving. Rectangular. 3¹⁵⁄₁₆ in. by 4⁹⁄₁₆ in. ☆ Stauffer 747. Stauffer lists this engraving as having an entry and publication line reading: "Entered according to Act of Congress, April 1ˢᵗ. 1813, and published at Philadelphia by Freeman & Pierie, of the state of Pennsylvania."

WILLIAM BIRCH (1755–1834) was born in Warwickshire, England. He came to Philadelphia in 1794, following a career in England as an enamel painter and engraver. In Philadelphia, Birch painted landscapes in water-colors and miniatures in enamel, and also engraved plates. His reputation as an American engraver is largely based upon his *Views of Philadelphia*, drawn and engraved in 1798–1800 in association with his son, Thomas Birch, later well known as a landscape and marine painter. Birch later issued a smaller series of plates showing American country seats. He died in Philadelphia.

249

Comodore Decatur. ☆ *L White M Osborn*

Stipple engraving. Profile bust. 5½ in. by 4 1/16 in. ☆ Stauffer 2376.

250

Commodore Decatur of the U. States Navy. ☆ *Sold by J. Kneass Copper-plate Printer Nº. 125 Market St. Philadelphia.*

Stipple engraving. Vignette with wreath at bottom. 4½ in. by 4¾ in.

251

Commodore Decatur. Destroyed the Frigate Philadelphia 1804 — Captured & brought in the British Frigate Macedonian 1812. Inscribed on a ribbon: *Free Trade & Sailors Rights* ☆ *Design'd & Acquatinted by Strickland* ☆ *Philadelphia Published by John Kneass Copperplate Printer.*

Line engraving with aquatinted vignette. Olive branch and ribbon below. 4¾ in. by 5 in. ☆ Stauffer 3046.

252

Stephen Decatur Esqᵉ. of the United States Navy. ☆ Artist and engraver not named.

Stipple engraving. Circular. 3¼ in. in diameter. Title in circular border.

253

Stephen Decatur Esq. ☆ *Painted by Mʳˢ. Plantou a few days before his death — Engraved by C. Goodman & R. Piggott.* ☆ *Published as the Act directs June 1820 by Mʳˢ. Plantou Nº. 110 So. 4ᵗʰ. St. Philadª.*

Stipple engraving. Oval. 6¾ in. by 5⅞ in. Portrait rests on wreath, flags, anchor, etc. ☆ Stauffer 1130.

CHARLES GOODMAN (circa 1790–1830) was a pupil of David Edwin in Philadelphia, the city of his birth. He became a skillful engraver in stipple. Subsequently he went into the engraving business with a fellow apprentice, Robert Piggott, establishing the firm of Goodman & Piggott in Philadelphia. This concern produced a considerable number of engraved portraits.

JESSE D. ELLIOTT

Jesse D. Elliott was born in Hagerstown, Md. on July 14, 1782. In 1804, he was appointed a Midshipman by President Thomas Jefferson. He served in various capacities in the Navy until the War of 1812, during which he was made Master Commandant in 1813 for his courageous action in capturing the British ships *Detroit* and *Caledonia* in the Niagara River.

In the famous Battle of Lake Erie Elliott commanded the brig *Niagara*, serving as second in command under Oliver H. Perry. A controversy which continued for many years arose over Elliott's conduct during this battle, it being thought by some that he failed to support the *Lawrence* sufficiently by not promptly bringing the *Niagara* actively into the engagement. A court of inquiry found Elliott not at fault. He continued as an officer in the Navy for many years, eventually commanding the frigate *Constitution* in 1838. Elliott died on December 10, 1845.

254

*Capt*ⁿ. *J. D. Elliott U. S. Navy.* ☆ *Edwin sc.*

Stipple engraving. Oval. 3 in. by 2¼ in. Second state. ☆ Stauffer 757ii.

First state incorrectly gave Elliott's name as "Captⁿ. M. C. Elliott". ☆ Stauffer 757i.

ESEK HOPKINS

Esek Hopkins, the first Commander-in-Chief of the Continental Navy, was born at Scituate, R. I., in 1718. He went to sea at the age of twenty. By 1741, he had under his direction a fleet of seventeen merchantmen. During the Seven Years' War he served as captain of a privateer. He was ranked as one of the leading Colonial seamen.

At the commencement of the Revolutionary War, Hopkins was commissioned as a General by his native State of Rhode Island. On December 22, 1775, he was appointed "Commander-in-Chief" of the Continental Navy, then recently authorized by the Continental Congress. His fleet consisted of eight converted merchant ships. John Paul Jones was a lieutenant on board the *Alfred*, Hopkins's flagship.

In February 1776, this squadron under Commodore Hopkins sailed on an expedition to the Bahamas for the purpose of capturing a large quantity of powder at Nassau on New Providence Island. Hopkins took possession of Nassau and seized many essential munitions of war, but only a small part of the desired supply of gunpowder.

On the return voyage, the fleet made prizes of a few British vessels. Near the Rhode Island coast, the British ship *Glasgow* was encountered. After disabling two of the Continental ships, the British man-of-war escaped. Hopkins was severely criticized for permitting the enemy to get away, and in 1777 was dismissed from his command by Congress. Historians believe that this action was unwise and deprived the Navy of the services of an officer possessing both experience and initiative. Hopkins died at Providence, R. I., in 1802.

The title of "Commander-in-Chief of the Fleet" was never revived after the dismissal of Hopkins.

255

Hopkins Commandant en Chef la Flotte Americaine. ☆ Inscribed on flags: *Don't tread upon me—Liberty tree—An Appeal to God.* ☆ *Dupin sculp.* ☆ *A Paris chez Esnauts et Rapilly, rue S^t. Jacques a la Ville de Coutances. A.P.D.R.*

Line engraving. 6⅛ in. by 4¼ in.

256

Admiral Hopkins Commendeur en Chef, de Flotte Americaine des XIII Provinces unies. ☆ *peint par Wilckenson a Boston.* ☆ *Se vend a Londres chez Thom. Hart.* Mezzotint. 8 in. by 6⅜ in.

ISAAC HULL

Isaac Hull was born at Shelton, Conn., on March 9, 1773. He went to sea at the age of fourteen and when nineteen was in command of a ship. In 1798, he became a Lieutenant in the United States Navy and served on board the frigate

Constitution. In the War with Tripoli, he commanded the *Enterprise* and subsequently the *Argus.*

By 1810, Hull had returned to and was in command of the *Constitution.* On August 19, 1812, the famous action with the *Guerrière* was fought and won, the first important naval battle of the War of 1812. After a long and honorable career in our Navy, which included service as a Naval Commissioner from 1815 to 1817, Hull died on February 13, 1843, at Philadelphia.

257

This Portrait of Captn*. Isaac Hull, of the United States Navy, also the representation of the most interesting scene during the Action, between the United States Frigate* Constitution, *and his Britannic Majesty's Frigate* Guerriere, *is most respectfully dedicated to the People of the United States, by their fellow Citizen, T. W. Freeman.* ☆ Large portrait of Capt. Isaac Hull at top. ☆ Vignette below of the engagement between the *Constitution* and the *Guerrière.* ☆ *Gilbert Stuart Esq*[r]*. Pinxit. The Vignette from an Original Drawing under the direction of Capt*[n]*. Hull.* ☆ *Published at Philadelphia, & Entered according to Act of Congress, the 1*[st]*. day of February 1813, by Freeman & Pierie, of the State of Pennsylvania.*

Mezzotint. Rectangular. 19½ in. by 13½ in. Colored by hand. ☆ Stauffer 1165. Stauffer attributes this engraving to George Graham, but states this attribution is disputed.

258

Isaac Hull Esq[r]*. of the United States Navy* ☆ Artist and engraver not named. Stipple engraving. Circular. 3⁵⁄₁₆ in. diameter. Title in circular border.

259

Captain I. Hull Eluded the British Fleet July 1812—Captured the Guerriere Aug. 1812. Inscribed on a ribbon: *First in Victory First in Battle.* ☆ *Aquatinted by W. Strickland.* ☆ *Published by John Kneass Phila.*

Aquatint. Vignette, with laurel branches and a ribbon. 6⅜ in. by 6⁷⁄₁₆ in. ☆ Second state, with publication line. ☆ Stauffer 3047.

260

Isaac Hull Esq[r]*. of the United States Navy* ☆ *G. Stuart Pinx*[t]*. D. Edwin sc.* ☆ *Engraved for the Analectic Magazine*

Stipple engraving. Rectangular. 3⁹⁄₁₆ in. by 2 ¹⁵⁄₁₆ in. ☆ First state. ☆ Stauffer 780i.

JACOB JONES

Jacob Jones was born near Smyrna, Del., in March 1768. He studied medicine, but found practice as a physician uncongenial. In 1799, at the age of thirty-one, he entered the United States Navy as a Midshipman. He was a Lieutenant on board the frigate *Philadelphia* when she grounded off Tripoli in 1803 and was captured. For twenty months thereafter he was held as a captive in Tripoli.

Jones was commander of the sloop-of-war *Wasp* when she fought and captured the British sloop-of-war *Frolic* on October 18, 1812. Both these vessels were captured later that day by the British 74-gun ship *Poictiers*, and Jones was taken to Bermuda as a prisoner. He was exchanged in 1813, however, and became commander of the frigate *Macedonian*. In 1814, he was transferred to Lake Ontario, where he commanded the *Mohawk* until the close of the War of 1812. Jones died on August 3, 1850.

261

Captain Jones Commander of the Macedonian—The Captur'd Frolick ☆ Artist and engraver not named. ☆ *Published by J. Kneass 125 Market St Phil*ª.

Line engraving. Vignette, with hand-tinted wreath and ribbon below. 4¼ in. by 4¼ in.

262

*Jacob Jones Esq*ʳ. *of the United States Navy.* ☆ Artist and engraver not named. ☆ *à Paris Ch. Bance Editeur, Rue J. J. Rousseau, N*º. *10*

Stipple engraving. Circular. 3⅛ in. diameter. Title in circular border.

263

*Jacob Jones Esq*ʳ. *of the United States Navy.* ☆ *Remb*ᵗ. *Peale P*ᵗ. *D. Edwin sc.* *Engrav'd for the Analectic Magazine.* ☆ *Entered according to act of Congress.*

Stipple engraving. Rectangular. 3¾ in. by 3¹⁄₁₆ in. ☆ Stauffer 793.

JOHN PAUL JONES

John Paul Jones was born in Scotland on July 6, 1747. His family name was Paul. He went to sea as a youth and at the age of eighteen had become a first mate. His early service was on various merchant vessels and slave ships. Jones came to America to live about 1769.

Soon after the Revolution began, Jones was commissioned on December 7, 1775, a Lieutenant in the new Continental Navy. He first served on the *Alfred* under Commodore Esek Hopkins. In this capacity he participated in 1776 in the capture of Nassau in the Bahamas and in the encounter with the British ship *Glasgow*.

On May 10, 1776, Jones was promoted to a captaincy, and in the following year was placed in command of the sloop-of-war *Ranger*. He soon sailed for France. The first raiding cruise of the *Ranger* was successful, her most celebrated exploit being the capture of the British sloop-of-war *Drake* in April 1778. Jones was given command of the *Bon Homme Richard* on February 4, 1779, and provided with a squadron of five ships. The famous action with the *Serapis* was fought off Flamborough Head on September 23, 1779.

Later Jones served as commanding officer of the fleet of Catherine the Great of Russia. He died at Paris on July 18, 1792. In 1905 his body was removed from Paris and later was placed in one of the buildings of the Naval Academy at Annapolis, Md.

264

John Paul Jones. Commodore au Service des Etats-Unis de l'Amérique, tel qu'il était dans le combat du 23. 7ᵇʳᵉ 1779. contre le Comodore Pearson. ☆ Son Vaisseau le bon home Richard montait 40. canons. le Vaisseau Anglais le Serapis 44. avait encore l'avantage du calibre, et la légèrté. le Comodore P. Jones, par se maneuvre engagea le Beaupré de l'enemi, et s'empara du Serapis en le combattant bord à bord pendant 2. heures 3/4. l'Action dura 3. heures et 1/4. Le bon home Richard coula le lendemain. ☆ Dessiné par C: Notté. Gravé par Carl Guttenberg. ☆ a Paris chez Guttenberg rue Sᵗ Hyacinthe la 2ᵐᵉ porte par la place Sᵗ Michel.

Line engraving. Rectangular. 10⅞ in. by 9¼ in. ☆ Presentation copy inscribed in handwriting: "à Monsieur de Bouschman par Son Servt. C. Guttenberg. 1781. 7ᵇʳᵉ."

265

Iohann Paul Jones, Befehlshaber einer Schwadron in Diensten Der 13, Vereinigten Provinzen von Nord Amerika. 1779. View of a naval action in the distance at the left. ☆ *I. E. Haid Sculp* ☆ *Zu finden in Augsburg beÿ I. I. Haid u. John.*

Mezzotint. Rectangular. 12³⁄₁₆ in. by 9⅝ in. ☆ The copy of this engraving included in the exhibition is a proof before all letters.

266

Capt. Paul Jones ☆ From an Original Drawing taken from the Life, on board the Serapis. ☆ London, Pub^d. Octr. 22, 1779, by Thos. Macklin, N°. 1, Lincolns Inn Fields.

Line engraving. Oval. 8³⁄₁₆ in. by 6⁹⁄₁₆ in.

267

Paul Jones the Pirate. ☆ Undated.

Pub. by A. Park, 47, Leonard S^t. Tabernacle Walk, London.

Woodcut. 7³⁄₁₆ in. by 5¹¹⁄₁₆ in. Colored by hand.

268

Capt. Paul Jones shooting a Sailor who had attempted to strike his Colours in an Engagement. ☆ Artist and engraver not named. ☆ London, Printed for R. Sayer & J. Bennett, Map & Printsellers. ☆ N°. 53, Fleet Street, as the Act directs, 1st. Jany. 1780.

Mezzotint. 12⅞ in. by 9⅞ in. Colored by hand.

269

Paul Jones shooting a Sailor who had attempted to strike his Colours in an Engagement. ☆ From the Original Picture by John Collet, in the possession of Carington Bowles. ☆ Printed for & Sold by Carington Bowles, at his Map & Print Warehouse, N°. 69 in S^t. Pauls Church Yard, London. ☆ Published as the Act directs, 2³ Decr. 1779

Mezzotint. 12¾ in. by 9⅞ in. Colored by hand. ☆ Different scene from that shown in the preceding print.

269 a

M^r. Goff as Paul Jones. N°. 98. New Series ☆ London, Published April, 9, 1832, by Orlando Hodgson, 10, Cloth Fair.

Woodcut. 8½ in. by 7⅛ in. Colored by hand and decorated with tinsel.

James Lawrence was born in Burlington, N. J., on October 1, 1781. After studying navigation, he became a Midshipman in 1798 and a Lieutenant in 1802. At Tripoli, he was second in command at the attack upon that city and at the daring exploit of the burning of the frigate *Philadelphia*. Between 1805 and 1812 Lawrence served as Lieutenant on the frigate *Constitution* and then commanded the ships *Vixen*, *Wasp*, *Argus* and *Hornet*, successively.

On February 24, 1813, the sloop-of-war *Hornet* under the command of Lawrence captured the British brig *Peacock*. He was advanced to the rank of Captain and ordered to take the frigate *Chesapeake*, his new command, to sea to intercept British shipping. Upon sailing from Boston on June 1, 1813, Lawrence chose immediately to engage the British frigate *Shannon*, then lying off shore in wait for him. The *Chesapeake* was captured in an action lasting only fifteen minutes. Lawrence was mortally wounded. On being carried below, he uttered his last command : "Don't give up the Ship." Lawrence died on June 4, 1813.

270

James Lawrence, Esqr. late Captⁿ. in the United States Navy. Obit. in Frigate Chesapeake, June 5th. 1813. Act. 32. "Dont give up the Ship" ☆ *Stuart pinx^t. Leney fc^t.* ☆ *Engraved by permission from the Original Picture in the possession of his family, 1813.* ☆ *Published by John Dixey N°. 51 Chatham Street. Printed by A. G. Reynolds.*

Stipple engraving. Rectangular. 5¹⁄₁₆ in. by 4¹⁄₁₆ in. ☆ Second State. Stauffer 1800ii.

271

James Lawrence Esqr. Late of the United States Navy ☆ Artist and engraver not named.

Stipple engraving. Circular. 3¼ in. in diameter. Title in circular border.

272

James Lawrence Esqr. late of the United States Navy. ☆ *Edwin sc.*

Stipple engraving. Circular. 2⅜ in. in diameter. ☆ Stauffer 804.

James Lawrence Esqr. Late of the United States Navy. Vignette of naval action below, inscribed: *Engraved by F. Kearney.* ☆ *Stuart Pinx^t. Edwin sc^t.* ☆ *Published by Moses Thomas, Philad^a. Entered according to Act of Congress December 1813.*

Stipple engraving. Rectangular. 4¾ in. by 3¹¹⁄₁₆ in. ☆ First state. ☆ Stauffer 802i.

274

Jas. Lawrence, Esquire. Died, June 4th, 1813. Aged 31 Years. Urn inscribed: *Sweet Sleep the Brave.* ☆ *Design'd & Engraved by A. Bowen.*

Line engraving, printed on silk. 5⅞ in. by 7½ in.

275

Captain Lawrence. Late of the American United States Frigate the Chesapeake, who was mortally wounded in the Engagement with His Majesty's Ship Shannon, Captn. B. V. Broke, off Boston Harbour the first of June, 1813. Engraved from a Portrait found in his possession at the time of his decease. This Print is respectfully dedicated to the British Nation, whose philanthrophy is such as to Esteem the Brave and Virtuous even in an Enemy. ☆ *Engraved by T. Williamson and Published by G. Webster, 21, White Lion Street, Pentonville.*

Stipple engraving. 2¼ in. by 2³⁄₁₆ in.

276

View of the fatal wounding of Captain James Lawrence on the deck of the *Chesapeake,* in a frame of laurel branches, with an eagle below holding a ribbon inscribed: *Don't Give Up The Ship.* Allegorical figure at each side. ☆ *W. Strickland del. & Sc.*

Aquatint. 11¼ in. by 14 in. In black and white.

A similar engraved scene is contained on a certificate of the Lawrence Benevolent Society of Philadelphia. Stauffer 3068.

THOMAS MACDONOUGH

Thomas Macdonough was born on December 31, 1783, at The Trap (now Macdonough), Maryland. In 1800, he entered the Navy as a Midshipman. He participated in the War with Tripoli and was a member of the daring group under Stephen Decatur, which burned the frigate *Philadelphia* at Tripoli. In 1805, he became senior lieutenant of the *Enterprise*.

Macdonough is best known for his achievements as commander of the fleet on Lake Champlain. His decisive defeat of the British fleet under Commodore George Downie near Plattsburg on September 11, 1814, stopped an impending British invasion and undoubtedly changed the whole course of the War of 1812. Macdonough is regarded by many authorities as the ablest American naval commander up to the time of the Civil War. He died on November 10, 1825.

277

Com. Thomas Macdonough of the United States Navy ☆ *Drawn & Engraved by T. Gimbrede N. York.*

Stipple engraving. Oval, with oak leaves above and two dolphins' heads below. 7⅞ in. by 8¾ in. ☆ Stauffer 1060.

278

Commodore McDonough Inscribed on a ribbon: *Heroe of Lake Champlain Designed & Aquatinted by* ——— ☆ *Pub. by P. Price J^r. Philad^a.*

Line engraving, Olive branch and ribbon below the portrait, also No. *82.* 4¾ in. by 4½ in. ☆ Attributed to George Delleker. See Stauffer 481.

OLIVER HAZARD PERRY

Oliver Hazard Perry was born in South Kingston, R. I., on August 20, 1785. After learning navigation as a boy at Newport, he followed his father in the Navy as a Midshipman in 1799, serving during the Quasi-War with France. He was an officer in the Mediterranean fleet during the War with Tripoli.

In 1812 Perry sought service on the Great Lakes under Commodore Chauncey. During the spring and summer of 1813 he supervised the building of a small fleet at Erie, Pa. The two most important ships were the brigs *Lawrence* and *Niagara*, both of which served as Perry's flagship during the Battle of Lake Erie. On September 10th, 1813, the battle off Put-in-Bay on Lake Erie was fought and decisively won by Perry. This victory gave to the

United States forces control of Lake Erie. Commodore Perry reported his victory to General William Henry Harrison with the famous message: "We have met the enemy and they are ours."

Perry died of yellow fever in Venezuela on August 23, 1819, while in command of a naval mission to that country.

279

Com^re. Oliver H. Perry, of the U. S. Navy. ☆ Eng^d. by Thos. Gimbrede. ☆ Published by Mich^l. H. Bowyer. 298 Bowery, New York

Stipple engraving. Oval, with oak leaves above and two dolphins' heads below. 12 in. by 8½ in. ☆ Stauffer 1076.

280

O. H. Perry Esqr. Hero of the Lake Inscribed on a ribbon: "We have met the enemy and they are ours." ☆ Design'd and Aquatinted by W. Strickland ☆ Philadelphia Published by John Kneass Copperplate Printer.

Aquatint. Vignette, with olive branch and ribbon. 5½ in. by 4¼ in.

281

Oliver H. Perry Esq. of the United States Navy. ☆ Artist and engraver not named.

Stipple engraving. Circular. 3⁵⁄₁₆ in. in diameter. Title in circular border.

282

Sept. 10th 1813. "We have met the enemy, and they are ours." Oliver H. Perry. ☆ I. Sanford Sc.

Stipple engraving. Rectangular. 4¹⁄₁₆ in. by 3 in. ☆ Stauffer 2740.

DAVID PORTER

David Porter was born in Boston, Mass., on February 1, 1780. He first went to sea in 1796 with his father, who was also a naval officer. Porter was a Midshipman on the frigate *Constellation*, when she captured the French frigate *L'Insurgente* during the Quasi-War with France. In the Tripolitan War, he was senior Lieutenant on the *Enterprise*, was wounded in the fighting on shore, and later captured when the frigate *Philadelphia* stranded before the City of Tripoli.

Porter was made a Captain in the Navy on July 2, 1812, and while in command of the frigate *Essex* during her famous cruise into the Pacific Ocean, took numerous prizes. On March 28, 1813, the *Essex* was captured off Valparaiso by the British ships *Phoebe* and *Cherub*.

In 1815 Porter commanded the *Fulton the First*, the first steam propelled vessel in our Navy. He resigned from the Navy in 1826 after having been court martialed for alleged injudicious handling of a situation in Puerto Rico. Porter later served in the Mexican Navy for three years and for twelve years as Consul General at Algiers. He died on March 3, 1843.

283

David Porter ☆ *L. Rados ins.*

Stipple engraving. Oval. 3⅛ in. by 2⁹⁄₁₆ in.

284

David Porter Esqᵉ. of the United States Navy ☆ Artist and engraver not named. ☆ *à Paris, chez Ch. Bance, Editeur, Rue J. J. Rousseau Nᵒ. 10*

Stipple engraving. Circular. 3³⁄₁₆ in. in diameter.

285

David Porter Esqᵉ. of the United States Navy ☆ *Wood Pinxt. Edwin sc.* ☆ *Engraved for Analectic Magazine Published by M. Thomas.*

Stipple engraving. 3³⁄₁₆ in. by 2¹⁵⁄₁₆ in. ☆ First state. Stauffer 853i.

EDWARD PREBLE

Edward Preble was born at Portland, Maine, on August 15, 1761, a son of General Jedidiah Preble, an officer of the Revolution. At the age of sixteen, he ran away to serve at sea on a privateer. In 1782, he was a Lieutenant under

Captain George Little on the Massachusetts cruiser, *Winthrop*. After the Revolution, Preble spent fifteen years in the merchant marine service, being once captured by pirates.

In 1799, Preble received a commission as Captain of the frigate, *Essex*, the first American man-of-war to show our flag beyond the Cape of Good Hope. Preble was in command of the third squadron sent to the Mediterranean in the War with Tripoli, and proved an able commander. The fact that he was superceded by Commodore Samuel Barron and thus prevented from attempting to carry out his plan for the capture of Tripoli is now regarded by naval historians as unfortunate. Preble died on August 25, 1807, at the age of 46.

286

Commodore Preble ☆ S. Harriss Sculp.

Stipple engraving. Oval. 3⁵⁄₁₆ in. by 2⁹⁄₁₆ in. ☆ Stauffer 1271.

JOHN RODGERS

John Rodgers, a member of a well-known American naval family, was born near Havre de Grace, Md. on July 11, 1771. His reading of books about the sea in childhood gave him the bent for a naval career, and he was a first mate before he was eighteen. After eleven years in the merchant marine service, he became an officer on the frigate *Constellation* and participated in the capture of the French frigate *L'Insurgente* on February 9, 1799.

Rodgers saw active service during the war against Tripoli, first being second in command of the American squadron in the Mediterranean and succeeding to the command of the fleet in 1805, at the time of the peace negotiations with Tripoli and Tunis.

In 1811, Rodgers was in command of the frigate *President*, when she engaged the British sloop *Little Belt*. This incident was a factor in bringing on the War of 1812. He was the ranking officer of the Navy in active service during the War of 1812. In 1821, he became the senior officer of the United States Navy, and in 1823 served for a brief time as acting Secretary of the Navy. Rodgers died in Philadelphia on August 1, 1838.

287

Commodore Rodgers. ☆ *Henry Williams pinx. John R. Smith Sculp*.

Stipple engraving. Oval. 4⁵⁄₁₆ in. by 3⁵⁄₁₆ in. ☆ Stauffer 2929.

288

John Rodgers Esq. of the United States Navy ☆ *Jarvis Pinx. Edwin sc.* ☆ *Engraved for the Analectic Magazine. Published by M. Thomas.*

Stipple engraving. Rectangular. 3⁹⁄₁₆ in. by 2⅞ in. ☆ First state. ☆ Stauffer 861i.

CHARLES STEWART

Charles Stewart was born at Philadelphia on July 28, 1778. Starting as a cabin boy at the age of thirteen, he soon became a merchant-ship captain. In 1798, he was made Lieutenant of the frigate *United States*. In 1800, he commanded the schooner *Experiment*. He went to the Mediterranean in 1802 as an officer of the frigate *Constellation*. He took part in the burning of the *Philadelphia* at Tripoli while assigned to the brig *Siren*.

In the War of 1812 Stewart commanded successively the *Argus*, *Hornet* and *Constellation*. Later, he was given command of the frigate *Constitution*, capturing the British ships *Cyane* and *Levant* on February 20, 1815. His long career in the Navy ended with his death on November 6, 1869.

289

Chs. Stewart Facsimile signature below. ☆ *Painted by J. P. Merrill Eng*ᵈ. *by J. Sartain Phil*ᵃ. ☆ *Engraved for the Gentleman's Magazine.*

Mezzotint. Rectangular. 5⁹⁄₁₆ in. by 4⁵⁄₁₆ in.

290

*Charles Stewart Esq*ʳ *Of the United States Navy* ☆ *Wood P*ᵗ. *Goodman Sculp*ᵗ

Stipple engraving. Oval in rectangle. 3¾ in. by 3¹⁄₁₆ in. ☆ Stauffer 1122ii.

THOMAS TRUXTON

Thomas Truxton was born near Hempstead, Long Island, on February 17, 1755. He went to sea at the age of twelve, and at fifteen was impressed and served briefly on H. M. S. *Prudent*. After obtaining his release, he became commander of a merchant ship at the age of twenty. He was an active privateersman during the Revolution. He commanded, among other ships, the *St. James*, which brought into Philadelphia the most valuable cargo entered there during the Revolution, and in connection with which Washington said that Truxton's services were worth a regiment.

As commander of the frigate *Constellation* Truxton captured the French frigate, *L'Insurgente* on February 9, 1799. On the night of February 1–2, 1800, the *Constellation* silenced the guns of the *Vengeance*, a vessel of considerably heavier gun power. Naval commentators have regretted that the services of Commodore Truxton were not utilized during the War of 1812. He died in 1822.

291

Commodore Truxton, of the Navy of the United States. ☆ *A. Robertson Pinx^t. C. Tiebout Sculp^t.*

Stipple engraving. Oval. 9$\frac{1}{16}$ in. by 7$\frac{7}{16}$ in. ☆ Stauffer 3193. Stauffer lists this engraving as having a publication line reading: "New York. Published by A. Robertson N°. 79 Liberty Str^t. & C. Tiebout N°. 28 Gold Street, Novem^r. 20th. 1799."

292

A Representation of the Medal presented by the United States to Thomas Truxton Esquire, and a copy of the Resolution of Congress. Obverse and reverse of the medal. Lower circle shows a naval action inscribed: *United States Frigate Constellation of 38 Guns pursues attacks and Vanquishes the French Ship La Vengeance of 54 Guns 1. Feb^r. 1800.* ☆ *A. Lawson sculp.*

Line and stipple engraving. Circles 2 in. in diameter. ☆ Stauffer 1687.

LEWIS WARRINGTON

Lewis Warrington was born on November 3, 1782 at Williamsburg, Virginia. On January 6, 1800, he was commissioned a Midshipman in the United States

Navy and assigned to the frigate *Chesapeake*. During the War with Tripoli he served as an officer on the *President*, *Vixen* and *Enterprise*, successively.

During the War of 1812 Warrington was on the frigate *Congress* as Lieutenant. Later he commanded the sloop-of-war *Peacock* when she captured the British brig *L'Epervier* on April 29, 1814. In the Indian Ocean he captured the *Nautilus* in June 1815. Following the war, he continued in varied naval services until his death on October 12, 1851.

293

Lewis Warrington Esqr. Of the United States Navy ☆ Jarvis Pinx^t. Gimbrede Sculp^t. ☆ Engraved for the Analectic Magazine ☆ Published by M. Thomas. Copy Right Secured According to Act of Congress October 2, 1815. Printed by Rogers & Esler

Stipple engraving. Rectangular. 4 in. by 3⁵⁄₁₆ in. ☆ Stauffer 1096.

Benedict Arnold, having commanded the Continental fleet at the battle on Lake Champlain in August 1776, is represented in this exhibition by the two following portraits:

294

Il traditore Generale Arnold. ☆ S. d'A. T. 27. Caratoni dis. ed inc.

Line engraving. 3¹¹⁄₁₆ in. by 2⁹⁄₁₆ in. Colored by hand.

295

Colonel Arnold. Commandirender General eines Corps Provincial Truppen in America. ☆ Nicht um hoher Gebuhrt sondern durch Thaten Gross. Wird Er von Freunden geliebt und von Feinden geehrt. ☆ Engraver and publisher not named.

Line engraving. 2³⁄₈ in. by 1⅝ in. ☆ Undated.

The engraved portraits of American naval commanders included in this exhibition are lent by Henry O. Havemeyer, Hall Park McCullough, Dr. Eugene H. Pool, the Estate of Francis P. Garvan, Irving S. Olds and Robert Fridenberg.

INDEX

(Historical accounts and biographical sketches are indicated by italic type.)

THE COMMITTEE ON PUBLICATIONS OF THE GROLIER CLUB
CERTIFIES THAT THIS COPY OF
THE UNITED STATES NAVY 1776–1815
IS ONE OF AN EDITION OF SEVEN HUNDRED COPIES
PRINTED BY THE GEORGE GRADY PRESS
IN THE MONTH OF NOVEMBER, 1942